Nus & Mimi
June 1965

Christmas Greetings — 1938
To Colin and Helen
from
The Bill Powels

—

UNCLE TOBY'S
CHRISTMAS BOOK
For All the Family

★

UNCLE TOBY'S
CHRISTMAS
BOOK

For All The Family

*"Everywhere, everywhere,
Christmas tonight."*

Illustrated by Julian Brazelton

PUBLISHERS

HARPER & BROTHERS

New York and London

1936

UNCLE TOBY'S CHRISTMAS BOOK

Copyright, 1936, by Harper & Brothers
Printed in the United States of America

SECOND EDITION

M-L

Uncle Toby
Presents:—

1 The Christmas Spirit as It Warms the Heart of All the World — A Collection of Yuletide Excerpts, Grave and Gay, Which Uncle Toby Has Chosen from Many Books and Many Lands.

CONTENTS

2 Uncle Toby's Favorite Christmas Poems — Familiar Lines to Bring Back Pleasant Memories, Together With Some Newcomers Which He Thinks Worthy of Such Genial Company.

3 Six Yuletide Short Stories Uncle Toby Has Chosen With Special Care — Smiles Here, Tears There, but the Christmas Spirit Everywhere. He Likes to Read the First of Them Out Loud.

4 Words and Music for Christmas Carols Uncle Toby Knows the Family Will Enjoy: All of Them Old Familiar Friends from Childhood Days.

5 How to Plan an Old-Fashioned Christmas: Uncle Toby's Suggestions for the Crèche, the Tree, the Table; Games, Decorations, Amusements of All Kinds, Tested Through the Years.

CONTENTS

6 Uncle Toby's Idea of What Makes the Perfect Christmas Dinner, and How to Go About Preparing It. He Took a Lot of Interest in This Section.

7 Before and After and With the Meal, Uncle Toby, as You Might Expect, Recommends Many Appetizing Beverages for Every Taste and Every Guest.

8 Because He Has a Particular Affection for Children, Uncle Toby Has Made a Special Selection of Unusual Christmas Tales for Boys and Girls.

9 Everyone Will Agree With Uncle Toby that No Child's Christmas Could Be Complete Without These Two Old Nursery Favorites, Read Aloud Before the Stockings Are Mysteriously Filled.

10 Good Christmas Plays for Children Are Rare, but Uncle Toby Has Found Two Which Are Sure to Bring Delight to Youthful Hearts.

11

Two Distinguished Christmas Sermons, Each in Its Own Way Presenting Anew the Message That Has Endured Two Thousand Years.

12

The Story of the Nativity as It Is Told in the New Testament, With Appropriate Prayers for Solemnizing Christmas in the Home.

A Family Christmas Service

For the Convenience of Many Who Have Found That a Simple Christmas-Eve Service Held in the Home Can Be Made a Joyful and Memorable Family Occasion, the Following Is Suggested:

UNCLE TOBY'S
CHRISTMAS BOOK
For All the Family

1

The Christmas Spirit as It Warms the Heart of
All the World—A Collection of Yuletide Ex-
cerpts, Grave and Gay, Which Uncle Toby Has
Chosen from Many Books and Many Lands.

Is There a Santa Claus?

An Editorial *by* FRANCIS P. CHURCH
reprinted from the "New York Sun," September 21, 1897

W E TAKE pleasure in answering at once and thus prominently the communication below, expressing at the same time our great gratification that its faithful author is numbered among the friends of *The Sun*:

> *Dear Editor:*
> *I am 8 years old.*
> *Some of my little friends say there is no Santa Claus.*
> *Papa says "If you see it in 'The Sun' it's so."*
> *Please tell me the truth, is there a Santa Claus?*
>
> > *Virginia O'Hanlon,*
> > *115 West 95th Street,*
> > *New York City.*

Virginia, your little friends are wrong. They have been affected by the skepticism of a skeptical age. They do not believe except they see. They think that nothing can be which is not comprehensible by their little minds. All minds, Virginia, whether they be men's or children's, are little. In this great universe of ours man is a mere insect, an ant, in his intellect, as compared with the boundless world about him, as measured by the intelligence capable of grasping the whole of truth and knowledge.

Yes, Virginia, there is a Santa Claus. He exists as certainly as love and generosity and devotion exist, and you know that they abound and give to your life its highest beauty and joy. Alas! how dreary would be the world if there were no Santa Claus! It would be as dreary as if there were no Virginias. There would be no childlike faith, then, no poetry, no romance to make tolerable this existence. We should have no enjoyment, except in sense and sight. The eternal light with which childhood fills the world would be extinguished.

2

Not believe in Santa Claus! You might as well not believe in fairies! You might get your papa to hire men to watch in all the chimneys on Christmas Eve to catch Santa Claus, but even if they did not see Santa Claus coming down, what would that prove? Nobody sees Santa Claus, but that is no sign that there is no Santa Claus. The most real things in the world are those that neither children nor men can see. Did you ever see fairies dancing on the lawn? Of course not, but that's no proof that they are not there. Nobody can conceive or imagine all the wonders there are unseen and unseeable in the world.

You tear apart the baby's rattle and see what makes the noise inside, but there is a veil covering the unseen world which not the strongest man, nor even the united strength of all the strongest men that ever lived, could tear apart. Only faith, fancy, poetry, love, romance, can push aside that curtain and view and picture the supernal beauty and glory beyond. Is it all real? Ah, Virginia, in all this world there is nothing else real and abiding.

No Santa Claus! Thank God he lives, and he lives forever. A thousand years from now, Virginia, nay, ten times ten thousand years from now, he will continue to make glad the heart of childhood.

Mr. Pickwick's Christmas

By CHARLES DICKENS

MR. WELLER, Emma, and the fat boy repaired to Mr. Wardle's large kitchen, in which the family, including Mr. Pickwick, were by this time assembled, according to annual custom on Christmas Eve, observed by old Wardle's forefathers from time immemorial.

From the centre of the ceiling of this kitchen old Wardle had just suspended, with his own hands, a huge branch of mistletoe, and this same branch of mistletoe instantaneously gave rise to a scene of general and most delightful struggling and confusion; in the midst of which, Mr. Pickwick, with a gallantry that would have done honour to a descendant of Lady Tollimglower herself, took the old lady by the hand, led her beneath the mystic branch, and saluted her in all courtesy and decorum. The old lady submitted to this piece of practical politeness with all the dignity which befitted so important and serious a solemnity; but the younger ladies, not being so thoroughly imbued with a superstitious veneration for the custom, or imagining that the value of a salute is very much enhanced if it cost a little trouble to obtain it, screamed and struggled, and ran into corners, and threatened and remonstrated, and did everything but leave the room, until some of the less adventurous gentlemen were on the point of desisting, when they all at once found it useless to resist any longer, and submitted to be kissed with a good grace. Mr. Winkle kissed the young lady with the black eyes, and Mr. Snodgrass kissed Emily, and Mr. Weller, not being particular about the form of being under the mistletoe, kissed Emma and the other female servants just as he caught them. As to the poor relations, they kissed everybody, not even excepting the plainer portion of the young-lady visitors, who, in their excessive confusion, ran right under the mistletoe, as soon as it was hung up, without knowing it! Wardle stood with his back to the fire, surveying the whole

4

scene with the utmost satisfaction; and the fat boy took the opportunity of appropriating to his own use, and summarily devouring, a particularly fine mince-pie that had been carefully put by for somebody else.

Now the screaming had subsided, and faces were in a glow, and curls in a tangle, and Mr. Pickwick, after kissing the old lady as before mentioned, was standing under the mistletoe, looking with

a very pleased countenance on all that was passing around him when the young lady with the black eyes, after a little whispering with the other young ladies, made a sudden dart forward, and putting her arm round Mr. Pickwick's neck, saluted him affectionately on the left cheek; and before Mr. Pickwick distinctly knew what was the matter, he was surrounded by the whole body, and kissed by every one of them.

It was a pleasant thing to see Mr. Pickwick in the centre of the group, now pulled this way and then that, and first kissed on the chin, and then on the nose, and then on the spectacles, and to hear the peals of laughter which were raised on every side; but it was a still more pleasant thing to see Mr. Pickwick, blinded shortly afterwards with a silk handkerchief, falling up against the wall, and scrambling into corners, and going through all the mysteries of blindman's buff, with the utmost relish for the game, until at last he caught one of the poor relations, and then had to evade the blind-man himself, which he did with a nimbleness and agility that elicited the admiration and applause of all beholders. The poor relations caught the people who they thought would like it, and when the game flagged got caught themselves. When they were all tired of blind-man's buff, there was a great game at snap-dragon; and when fingers enough were burnt with that, and all the raisins were gone, they sat down by the huge fire of blazing logs to a substantial supper, and a mighty bowl of wassail, something smaller than an ordinary wash-house copper, in which the hot apples were hissing and bubbling with a rich look and jolly sound that were perfectly irresistible.

"This," said Mr. Pickwick, looking round him—"this is, indeed, comfort."

"Our invariable custom," replied Mr. Wardle. "Everybody sits down with us on Christmas Eve, as you see them now—servants and all; and here we wait, until the clock strikes twelve, to usher Christmas in, and beguile the time with forfeits and old stories. —Trundle, my boy, rake up the fire."

Up flew the bright sparks in myriads as the logs were stirred. The deep red blaze sent forth a rich glow, that penetrated into the farthest corner of the room, and cast its cheerful tint on every face.

"Come," said Wardle, "a song—a Christmas song! I'll give you one, in default of a better."

"Bravo!" said Mr. Pickwick.

"Fill up," cried Wardle. "It will be two good hours before you see the bottom of the bowl through the deep rich colour of the wassail; fill up all round, and now for the song."

Thus saying, the merry old gentleman, in a good, round, sturdy voice, commenced without more ado:

> My song I troll out for CHRISTMAS stout,
> The hearty, the true, and the bold;
> A bumper I drain, and with might and main
> Give three cheers for this Christmas old!

We'll usher him in with a merry din
That shall gladden his joyous heart,
And we'll keep him up while there's bite or sup,
And in fellowship good we'll part.

This song was tumultuously applauded—for friends and dependents make a capital audience—and the poor relations especially were in perfect ecstasies of rapture. Again was the fire replenished, and again went the wassail round.

A Miserable, Merry Christmas

By LINCOLN STEFFENS

WHAT interested me in our new neighborhood was not the
school, nor the room I was to have in the house all to myself,
but the stable which was built back of the house. My father let me
direct the making of a stall, a little smaller than the other stalls,
for my pony, and I prayed and hoped and my sister Lou believed
that that meant that I would get the pony, perhaps for Christmas.
I pointed out to her that there were three other stalls and no
horses at all. This I said in order that she should answer it. She
could not. My father, sounded, said that some day we might have
horses and a cow; meanwhile a stable added to the value of a
house. "Some day" is a pain to a boy who lives in and knows only
"now." My good little sisters, to comfort me, remarked that
Christmas was coming and grown-ups were always talking about
it, asking you what you wanted and then giving you what they
wanted you to have. Though everybody knew what I wanted, I
told them all again. My mother knew that I told God, too, every
night. I wanted a pony, and to make sure that they understood,
I declared that I wanted nothing else.

"Nothing but a pony?" my father asked.

"Nothing," I said.

"Not even a pair of high boots?"

That was hard. I did want boots, but I stuck to the pony. "No,
not even boots."

"Nor candy? There ought to be something to fill your stocking
with, and Santa Claus can't put a pony into a stocking."

That was true, and he couldn't lead a pony down the chimney,
either. But no, "All I want is a pony," I said. "If I can't have a
pony, give me nothing, nothing."

Now I had been looking myself for the pony I wanted, going
to sales stables, inquiring of horsemen, and I had seen several that

would do. My father let me "try" them. I tried so many ponies that I was learning fast to sit a horse. I chose several, but my father always found some fault with them. I was in despair. When Christmas was at hand I had given up all hope of a pony, and on Christmas Eve I hung up my stocking along with my sisters'. They were so happy that I caught some of their merriment. I speculated on what I'd get; I hung up the biggest stocking I had, and we all went reluctantly to bed to wait till morning. Not to sleep; not right away. We were told that we must not only sleep promptly, we must not wake up till seven-thirty the next morning —or if we did, we must not go to the fireplace for our Christmas. Impossible.

We did sleep that night, but we woke up at six A.M. We lay in our beds and debated through the open doors whether to obey till, say, half-past six. Then we bolted. I don't know who started it, but there was a rush. We all disobeyed; we raced to disobey and get first to the fireplace in the front room downstairs. And there they were, the gifts, all sorts of wonderful things, mixed-up piles of presents; only, as I disentangled the mess, I saw that my stocking was empty; it hung limp; not a thing in it; and under and around it—nothing.

My sisters had knelt down, each by her pile of gifts; they were squealing with delight, till they looked up and saw me standing there in my nightgown with nothing. They left their piles to come to me and look with me at my empty place. Nothing. They felt my stocking: nothing.

I don't remember whether I cried at that moment, but my sisters did. They ran with me back to my bed, and there we all cried till I became indignant. That helped some. I got up, dressed, and driving my sisters away, I went alone out into the yard, down to the stable, and there, all by myself, I wept. My mother came out to me by and by; she found me in my pony stall, sobbing on the floor, and she tried to comfort me. But I heard my father outside; he had come part way with her, and she was having some sort of angry quarrel with him. She tried to comfort me; besought me to come to breakfast. I could not; I wanted no comfort and no breakfast. She left me and went on into the house with sharp words for my father.

I don't know what kind of breakfast the family had. My sisters said it was "awful." They were ashamed to enjoy their own toys. They came to me, and I was rude. I ran away from them. I went around to the front of the house, sat down on the steps, and, the crying over, I ached. I was wronged, I was hurt—I can feel now what I felt then, and I am sure that if one could see the wounds upon our hearts, there would be found still upon mine a scar from that terrible Christmas morning. And my father, the practical joker, he must have been hurt, too, a little. I saw him looking out of the window. He was watching me or something for an hour or two, drawing back the curtain ever so little lest I catch him, but I saw his face, and I think I can see now the anxiety upon it, the worried impatience.

After—I don't know how long—surely an hour or two—I was brought to the climax of my agony by the sight of a man riding a pony down the street, a pony and a brand-new saddle; the most beautiful saddle I ever saw, and it was a boy's saddle; the man's feet were not in the stirrups; his legs were too long. The outfit was perfect; it was the realization of all my dreams, the answer to all my prayers. A fine new bridle, with a light curb bit. And the pony! As he drew near, I saw that the pony was really a small horse, what we called an Indian pony, a bay, with black mane and tail, and one white foot and a white star on his forehead. For such a horse as that I would have given, I could have forgiven, anything.

But the man, a disheveled fellow with a blackened eye and a fresh-cut face, came along, reading the numbers on the houses, and, as my hopes—my impossible hopes—rose, he looked at our door and passed by, he and the pony, and the saddle and the bridle. Too much. I fell upon the steps, and, having wept before, I broke now into such a flood of tears that I was a floating wreck when I heard a voice.

"Say, kid," it said, "do you know a boy named Lennie Steffens?" I looked up. It was the man on the pony, back again, at our horse block.

"Yes," I spluttered through my tears. "That's me."

"Well," he said, "then this is your horse. I've been looking all over for you and your house. Why don't you put your number where it can be seen?"

"Get down," I said, running out to him.

He went on saying something about "ought to have got here at seven o'clock; told me to bring the nag here and tie him to your post and leave him for you. But, hell, I got into a drunk—and a fight—and a hospital, and——"

"Get down," I said.

He got down, and he boosted me up to the saddle. He offered to fit the stirrups to me, but I didn't want him to. I wanted to ride. "What's the matter with you?" he said, angrily. "What you crying for? Don't you like the horse? He's a dandy, this horse. I know him of old. He's fine at cattle; he'll drive 'em alone."

I hardly heard, I could scarcely wait, but he persisted. He adjusted the stirrups, and then, finally, off I rode, slowly, at a walk, so happy, so thrilled, that I did not know what I was doing. I did not look back at the house or the man. I rode off up the street, taking note of everything—of the reins, of the pony's long mane, of the carved leather saddle. I had never see anything so beautiful. And mine! I was going to ride up past Miss Kay's house. But I noticed on the horn of the saddle some stains like rain-drops, so I turned and trotted home, not to the house but to the stable. There was the family, father, mother, sisters, all working for me, all happy. They had been putting in place the tools of my new business: blankets, currycomb, brush, pitchfork—everything, and there was hay in the loft.

"What did you come back so soon for?" somebody asked. "Why didn't you go on riding?"

I pointed to the stains. "I wasn't going to get my new saddle rained on," I said. And my father laughed. "It isn't raining," he said. "Those are not raindrops."

"They are tears," my mother gasped, and she gave my father a look which sent him off to the house. Worse still, my mother offered to wipe away the tears still running out of my eyes. I gave her such a look as she had given him, and she went off after my father, drying her own tears. My sisters remained and we all unsaddled the pony, put on his halter, led him to his stall, tied and fed him. It began really to rain; so all the rest of that memorable day we curried and combed that pony. The girls plaited his mane, forelock, and tail, while I pitchforked hay to him and curried and brushed, curried and brushed. For a change we brought him out to drink; we led him up and down, blanketed like a race-horse;

we took turns at that. But the best, the most inexhaustible fun, was to clean him. When we went reluctantly to our midday Christmas dinner, we all smelt of horse, and my sisters had to wash their faces and hands. I was asked to, but I wouldn't, till my mother bade me look in the mirror. Then I washed up—quick. My face was caked with the muddy lines of tears that had coursed over my cheeks to my mouth. Having washed away that shame, I ate my dinner, and as I ate I grew hungrier and hungrier. It was my first meal that day, and as I filled up on the turkey and the stuffing, the cranberries and the pies, the fruit and the nuts—as I swelled, I could laugh. My mother said I still choked and sobbed now and then, but I laughed, too; I saw and enjoyed my sisters' presents till—I had to go out and attend to my pony, who was there, really and truly there, the promise, the beginning, of a happy double life. And—I went and looked to make sure—there was the saddle, too, and the bridle.

But that Christmas, which my father had planned so carefully, was it the best or the worst I ever knew? He often asked me that; I never could answer as a boy. I think now that it was both. It covered the whole distance from broken-hearted misery to bursting happiness—too fast. A grown-up could hardly have stood it.

How Come Christmas?

By ROARK BRADFORD

SCENE: *Corner in rural Negro church by the stove. The stove is old, and the pipe is held approximately erect by guywires, but a cheerful fire is evident through cracks in the stove, and the woodbox is well filled. Six children sit on a bench which has been shifted to face the stove, and the Reverend stands between them and the stove. A hatrack on the wall supports sprigs of holly and one "plug" hat. A window is festooned with holly, long strips of red paper, and strings of popcorn. A small Christmas bell and a tiny American flag are the only "store bought" decorations.*

REVEREND—Well, hyar we is, chilluns, and hyar hit is Christmas. Now we all knows we's hyar 'cause hit's Christmas, don't we? But what I want to know is, who gonter tell me how come hit's Christmas?

WILLIE—'Cause old Sandy Claus come around about dis time er de year, clawin' all de good chilluns wid presents.

CHRISTINE—Dat ain't right, is hit, Revund? Hit's Christmas 'cause de Poor Little Jesus was bawned on Christmas, ain't hit, Revund?

REVEREND—Well, bofe er dem is mighty good answers. Old Sandy Claus do happen around about dis time er de year wid presents, and de Poor Little Jesus sho was bawned on Christmas Day. Now, de question is, did old Sandy Claus start clawin' chillun wid presents before de Poor Little Jesus got bawned, or did de Little Jesus git bawned before old Sandy Claus started gittin' around?

WILLIE—I bet old Sandy Claus was clawin' chilluns before de Poor Little Jesus started studdin' about gittin' bawned.

CHRISTINE—Naw, suh. De Little Jesus comed first, didn't he, Revund?

13

WILLIE—Old Sandy Claus is de oldest. I seed his pitchers and I seed Jesus' pitchers and old Sandy Claus is a heap de oldest. His whiskers mighty nigh tetch de ground.

DELIA—Dat ain't right. Old Methuselah is de oldest, ain't he, Revund? Cause de Bible say

> *Methuselah was de oldest man of his time.*
> *He lived nine hund'ed and sixty-nine.*
> *And he died and went to heaven in due time.*

REVEREND—Methuselah was powerful old, all right.

WILLIE—He wa'n't no older den old Sandy Claus, I bet. Old Sandy Claus got a heap er whiskers.

CHRISTINE—But de Poor Little Jesus come first. He was hyar before old man Methuselah, wa'n't he, Revund?

REVEREND—He been hyar a powerful long time, all right.

WILLIE—So has old Sandy Claus. He got powerful long whiskers.

DELIA—Moses got a heap er whiskers too.

REVEREND—Yeah, Moses was a mighty old man, too, but de p'int is, how come Christmas git started bein' Christmas? Now who gonter tell me? 'Cause hyar hit is Christmas Day, wid ev'ybody happy and rejoicin' about, and hyar is us, settin' by de stove in de wa'm churchhouse, tawkin' about hit. But ain't nobody got no idee how come hit start bein' Christmas?

WILLIE—You can't fool old Sandy Claus about Christmas. He know, don't he, Revund? He jest lay around and watch and see how de chilluns mind dey maw, and den de fust thing you know he got his mind make up about who been good and who been bad, and den he just hauls off and has hisse'f a Christmas.

CHRISTINE—Yeah, but how come he know hit's time to haul off and have hisse'f a Christmas?

WILLIE—'Cause any time old Sandy Claus make up his mind to have Christmas, well, who gonter stop him?

CHRISTINE—Den how come he don't never make up his mind ontwell de middle er winter? How come he don't make up his mind on de Fou'th er July? Ev'ybody git good around de Fou'th er July, jest like Christmas, so's dey kin go to de picnic. But

Sandy Claus ain't payin' no mind to dat cause hit ain't time for Christmas, is hit, Revund?

WILLIE—Cou'se he don't have Christmas on de Fou'th er July. 'Cause hit ain't no p'int in Sandy Claus clawin' ev'ybody when ev'ybody's goin' to de picnic, anyhow. Sandy Claus b'lieve in scatterin' de good stuff out, don't he, Revund? He say, "Well, hit ain't no p'int in me clawin' fo'ks when dey already havin' a good time goin' to de picnic. Maybe I better wait to de dead er winter when hit's too cold for de picnic." Ain't dat right, Revund?

REVEREND—Sandy Claus do b'lieve in scatterin' de good stuff about de seasons, Willie, and hit sho ain't no p'int in havin' Christmas on de Fou'th er July. 'Cause de Fou'th er July is got hit's own p'int. And who gonter tell me what de p'int er de Fou'th er July is?

CHORUS—

Old Gawge Wash'n'ton whupped de kaing,
And de eagle squalled, Let Freedom raing.

REVEREND—Dat's right. And dat was in de summertime, so ev'ybody went out and had a picnic 'cause dey was so glad dat Gawge Wash'n'ton whupped dat kaing. Now what's de p'int er Christmas?

WILLIE—Old Sandy Claus . . .

CHRISTINE—De Poor Little Jesus . . .

REVEREND—Well, hit seem like old Sandy Claus and de Poor Little Jesus bofe is mixed up in dis thing, f'm de way y'all chilluns looks at hit. And I reckon y'all is just about zackly right too. 'Cause dat's how hit is. Bofe of 'em is so mixed up in hit I can't tell which is which, hardly.

DELIA—Was dat before de Fou'th er July?

CHRISTINE—Cou'se hit was. Don't Christmas always come before de Fou'th er July?

WILLIE—Naw, suh. Hit's de Fou'th er July fust, and den hit's Christmas. Ain't dat right, Revund?

REVEREND—I b'lieve Christine got you dat time, Willie. Christmas do come before de Fou'th er July. 'Cause you see hit was at

Christmas when old Gawge Wash'n'ton got mad at de kaing 'cause de kaing was gonter kill de Poor Little Jesus. And him and de kaing fit f'm Christmas to de Fou'th er July before old Gawge Wash'n'ton finally done dat kaing up.

WILLIE—And Gawge Wash'n'ton whupped dat kaing, didn't he?

REVEREND—He whupped de stuffin' outn him. He whupped him f'm Balmoral to Belial and den back again. He jest done dat kaing up so bad dat he jest natchally put kaingin' outn style, and ev'y since den, hit ain't been no more kaings to 'mount to much.

You see, kaings was bad fo'ks. Dey was mean. Dey'd druther kill you den leave you alone. You see a kaing wawkin' down de road, and you better light out across de field, 'cause de kaing would wawk up and chop yo' haid off. And de law couldn't tetch him, cause he was de kaing.

So all de fo'ks got skeered er de kaing, 'cause dey didn't know how to do nothin' about hit. So ev'ybody went around, tryin' to stay on de good side of him. And all er dat is how come de Poor Little Jesus and Old Sandy Claus got mixed up wid gittin' Christmas goin'.

You see, one time hit was a little baby bawned name' de Poor Little Jesus, but didn't nobody know dat was his name yit. Dey knew he was a powerful smart and powerful purty little baby, but dey didn't know his name was de Poor Little Jesus. So, 'cause he was so smart and so purty, ev'ybody thought he was gonter grow up and be de kaing. So quick as dat news got spread around, ev'ybody jest about bust to git on de good side er de baby, 'cause dey figure efn dey start soon enough he'd grow up likin' 'em and not chop dey haids off.

So old Moses went over and give him a hund'ed dollars in gold. And old Methuselah went over and give him a diamond ring. And old Peter give him a fine white silk robe. And ev'ybody was runnin' in wid fine presents so de Poor Little Jesus wouldn't grow up and chop de haids off.

Ev'ybody but old Sandy Claus. Old Sandy Claus was kind er old and didn't git around much, and he didn't hyar de news dat de Poor Little Jesus was gonter grow up and be de kaing. So him and de old lady was settin' back by de fire one night, toastin' dey shins and tawkin' about dis and dat, when old Miz Sandy Claus up and remark, she say, "Sandy, I hyars Miss Mary got a brand new baby over at her house."

"Is dat a fack?" says Sandy Claus. "Well, well, hit's a mighty cold night to do anything like dat, ain't hit? But on de yuther hand, he'll be a heap er pleasure and fun for her next summer I reckon."

So de tawk went on, and finally old Sandy Claus remark dat hit was powerful lonesome around de house since all er de chilluns growed up and married off.

"Dey all married well," say Miz Sandy Claus, "and so I say, 'Good ruddance.' You ain't never had to git up and cyore dey colic and mend dey clothes, so you gittin' lonesome. Me, I love 'em all, but I'm glad dey's married and doin' well."

So de tawk run on like dat for a while, and den old Sandy Claus got up and got his hat. "I b'lieve," he say, "I'll drap over and see how dat baby's gittin' along. I ain't seed no chillun in so long I'm pyore hongry to lean my eyes up agin a baby."

"You ain't goin' out on a night like dis, is you?" say Miz Sandy Claus.

"Sho I'm goin' out on a night like dis," say Sandy Claus. "I'm pyore cravin' to see some chilluns."

"But hit's snowin' and goin' on," say Miz Sandy Claus. "You know yo' phthisic been develin' you, anyhow, and you'll git de chawley mawbuses sloppin' around in dis weather."

"No mind de tawk," say Sandy Claus. "Git me my umbrella and my overshoes. And you better git me a little somethin' to take along for a cradle gift, too, I reckon."

"You know hit ain't nothin' in de house for no cradle gift," say Miz Sandy Claus.

"Git somethin'," say Sandy Claus. "You got to give a new baby somethin', or else you got bad luck. Get me one er dem big red apples outn de kitchen."

"What kind er cradle gift is an apple?" say Miz Sandy Claus. "Don't you reckon dat baby git all de apples he want?"

"Git me de apple," say Sandy Claus. "Hit ain't much, one way you looks at hit. But f'm de way dat baby gonter look at de apple, hit'll be a heap."

So Sandy Claus got de apple and he lit out.

Well, when he got to Miss Mary's house ev'ybody was standin'
around givin' de Poor Little Jesus presents. Fine presents. Made
outn gold and silver and diamonds and silk, and all like dat. Dey
had de presents stacked around dat baby so high you couldn't
hardly see over 'em. So when ev'ybody seed old Sandy Claus come
in dey looked to see what he brang. And when dey seed he didn't
brang nothin' but a red apple, dey all laughed.

"Quick as dat boy grows up and gits to be de kaing," dey told
him, "he gonter chop yo' haid off."

"No mind dat," say Sandy Claus. "Y'all jest stand back." And
so he went up to de crib and he pushed away a handful er gold
and silver and diamonds and stuff, and handed de Poor Little
Jesus dat red apple. "Hyar, son," he say, "take dis old apple. See
how she shines?"

And de Poor Little Jesus reached up and grabbed dat apple in
bofe hands, and laughed jest as brash as you please!

Den Sandy Claus tuck and tickled him under de chin wid his
before finger, and say, "Goodly-goodly-goodly." And de Poor
Little Jesus laughed some more and he reached up and grabbed a
fist full er old Sandy Claus' whiskers, and him and old Sandy
Claus went round and round!

So about dat time, up stepped de Lawd. "I swear, old Sandy
Claus," say de Lawd. "Betwixt dat apple and dem whiskers, de
Poor Little Jesus ain't had so much fun since he been bawn."

So Sandy Claus stepped back and bowed low and give de Lawd
hy-dy, and say, "I didn't know ev'ybody was chiv-areein', or else
I'd a stayed at home. I didn't had nothin' much to bring dis time,
'cause you see how hit's been dis year. De dry weather and de
bull weevils got mighty nigh all de cotton, and de old lady been
kind er puny ——"

"Dat's all right, Sandy," say de Lawd. "Gold and silver have I
a heap of. But verily you sho do know how to handle yo'se'f
around de chilluns."

"Well, Lawd," say Sandy Claus, "I don't know much about
chilluns. Me and de old lady raised up fou'teen. But she done
most er de work. Me, I jest likes 'em and I manages to git along
wid 'em."

"You sho do git along wid 'em good," say de Lawd.

"Hit's easy to do what you likes to do," say Sandy Claus.

"Well," say de Lawd, "hit might be somethin' in dat, too. But de trouble wid my world is, hit ain't enough people which likes to do de right thing. But you likes to do wid chilluns, and dat's what I needs. So stand still and shet yo' eyes whilst I passes a miracle on you."

So Sandy Claus stood still and shet his eyes, and de Lawd r'ared back and passed a miracle on him and say, "Old Sandy Claus, live forever, and make my chilluns happy."

So Sandy Claus opened his eyes and say, "Thank you kindly, Lawd. But do I got to keep 'em happy all de time? Dat's a purty big job. Hit'd be a heap er fun, but still and at de same time ——"

"Yeah, I knows about chilluns, too," say de Lawd. "Chilluns got to fret and git in devilment ev'y now and den and git a whuppin' f'm dey maw, or else dey skin won't git loose so's dey kin grow. But you jest keep yo' eyes on 'em and make 'em all happy about once a year. How's dat?"

"Dat's fine," say Sandy Claus. "Hit'll be a heap er fun, too. What time er de year you speck I better make 'em happy, Lawd?"

"Christmas suit me," say de Lawd, "efn hit's all o.k. wid you."

"Hit's jest about right for me," say old Sandy Claus.

So ev'y since dat day and time old Sandy Claus been clawin' de chilluns on Christmas, and dat's on de same day dat de Poor Little Jesus got bawned. 'Cause dat's de way de Lawd runs things. O' cou'se de Lawd knowed hit wa'n't gonter be long before de Poor Little Jesus growed up and got to be a man. And when he done dat, all de grown fo'ks had him so's dey c'd moan they sins away and lay they burdens down on him, and git happy in they hearts. De Lawd made Jesus for de grown fo'ks. But de Lawd know de chilluns got to have some fun, too, so dat's how come hit's Sandy Claus and Christmas and all.

Christmas at the White House

PRESIDENT THEODORE ROOSEVELT *writes to* Master James A. Garfield

White House, Dec. 26, 1902.

JIMMIKINS:

. . . Yesterday morning at a quarter of seven all the children were up and dressed and began to hammer at the door of their mother's and my room, in which their six stockings, all bulging out with queer angles and rotundities, were hanging from the fireplace. So their mother and I got up, shut the window, lit the fire, (taking down the stockings, of course,) put on our wrappers and prepared to admit the children. But first there was a surprise for me, also for their good mother, for Archie had a little Christmas tree of his own, which he had rigged up with the help of one of the carpenters in a big closet; and we all had to look at the tree and each of us got a present off of it. There was also one present each for Jack, the dog, Tom Quartz, the kitten, and Algonquin, the pony, whom Archie would no more think of neglecting than I would neglect his brothers and sisters. Then all the children came into our bed and there they opened their stockings. Afterwards we got dressed and took breakfast, and then all went into the library, where each child had a table set for his bigger presents. Quentin had a perfectly delightful electric railroad, which had been rigged up for him by one of his friends, the White House electrician, who has been very good to all the children. Then Ted and I, with General Wood and Mr. Bob Ferguson, who was a lieutenant in my regiment, went for a three hours' ride; and all of us, including all the children, took lunch at the house with the children's aunt, Mrs. Captain Cowles—Archie and Quentin having their lunch at a little table with their cousin Sheffield. Late in the afternoon I played at single stick with General Wood and Mr. Ferguson. I am going to get your father to come on and try it soon. We have to try to hit as light as possible, but sometimes we hit hard, and to-day I have a bump over one eye and a swollen wrist. Then all our family and kinsfolk and Senator and Mrs. Lodge's family and kinsfolk had our Christmas dinner at the White House, and afterwards danced in the East Room, closing up with the Virginia Reel.

Another Roosevelt Christmas

An Entry in Young Teddy's Diary When He Was Eleven Years Old

Christmas Dec. 25th 1869 Rome

. . . Christmas! Christmas! hip, hip, hurrah!. I was awake at 4 and we all 4 children got up at a little befor 6 and went in to Mamas and Papas bed. I caught everrybody in saying "Merry Christmas." We then opened our stockings. They were nice and bulkey. I had 2 oranges and 5 kinds of candy in mine. I had a compas, themometer, 12 photographs, a cardinel's cap. A pair of gloves and a beautiful cravat. Gourd for a water flask. A little ivory box with amber cover and an ivory chammois. We then got dressed and looked over our presents. Then we said "merry Christmas" to Mr. Stevens. Then Papa and Mama came in (we had prayers) and then we had breakfast. We then went in to the parlor to our tables. The presents passed our upmost expectations. I had a beautiful hunt with all kinds of things in it. I received 2 lamps and an inkstand on the ancient pompeien style and a silver sabre, slippers, a gold helmet and cannon besides the ivory chammois. I have beautiful writing paper, a candle stick on the Antiuke stile. A mosaic 1,500 years old and 3 books, 2 watch cases, 9 big photographs and an ornament and pair of studs. I played with my hunt for an hour. When we went to St. Peters to see the Pope. We saw him after long waiting. We came home played and all of us had dinner. Then Mama and Papa went out. I am going to put up all my Christmas presents. The vallet and I have been trying to put to gether my puzzle map.

Santa Claus at the North Pole

By Richard Evelyn Byrd

I T WAS the night before Christmas. My plan for the first human flight across the North Pole was practically complete. To the world at large it was all a secret. Only a trusted few were in my confidence. Then without the slightest warning I found myself facing an unexpected crisis. Three people to whom I had told nothing suddenly and simultaneously confronted me with a terrific question. This question was delivered with the savage directness of a dagger thrust.

The three people were Katharine, Bolling, and Dickie Byrd, aged three, four and six, respectively.

The question was: "Daddy, will you see Santa Claus?"

It staggered me. Somehow they had learned their father was going to attempt an extraordinary thing.

Then I played the coward. I said: "I will tell you in the morning."

"Promise?" from all three at once.

"I promise."

Three small white figures ducked up the stairs. There was giggling and skylarking. Then a chiding voice we all loved:

" 'Twas the night before Christmas, and all through the house
Not a creature was stirring, not even a mouse . . ."

Out clicked a light. "I'm asleep!" shouted Junior.

"And I. And I," echoed the others.

Christmas morning dawned bright and clear and cold. We had the stockings in bed. There was a vast deal of thrills and chortling joy. But before the day was far along they all remembered their question. By now I was prepared. "No, I shan't see Santa Claus," I told Katharine and Bolling and Dickie. "But when I get back I'll tell you all about his place at the North Pole."

There, I had done it: I was committed. My fate was sealed

23

when Dickie, the elder, in the presence of the others gave me a penetrating look and said:

"But there is a Santa Claus, Daddy, isn't there?"

"Of course there is a Santa Claus!" I fairly shouted.

In that moment was created the greatest problem of my forthcoming polar flight. One who has not lied to a child could never understand. I had baldly and without reservation told my three babies something about which I myself was not sure. I had told them there was a Santa Claus. How did I know? I had never seen him. But perhaps in the course of this great adventure I should find that after all Santa Claus does exist.

It began to look that way when, after many disappointments, some fine generous friends gave me the money I needed for my voyage.

A splendid gentleman made it possible for me a few weeks later to get the ship I wanted.

"Won't he do?" I asked the mother of the three whom I had promised to satisfy. "He even looks like Santa Claus. I think I could get him to come around and talk to the babies."

But she spurned the plan. "He's just a man who helped you out, isn't he? He isn't Santa Claus." She came a step nearer. "Surely you believe there is a Santa Claus, don't you?" she said, a little fiercely, I thought.

I mopped my brow. It was April now and no weather for such talk. Also things weren't going as well as they might.

"I don't know whether there is a Santa Claus or not," I said lamely.

A few days later the little steamer *Chantier* with my plane and a crew of brave volunteers set sail. For two weeks she plowed her way northward toward the region of eternal ice and snow. She reached Spitzbergen safely, and we landed the plane through grinding floes.

Finally we hopped off for the Pole. Up into the blue sky our huge noisy bird winged her way. My good friend Floyd Bennett sat at the wheel. Calm and unafraid he held our course northward while I consulted the instruments of flight on which our lives depended.

Behind us dropped the narrow, berg-dotted harbor in which lay the ship. To our right, slipping swiftly by, were mountain peaks dazzling white in their cloaks of snow. Presently they too were gone. We emerged into a strange world, a world of blue sky above and white ice below.

There was nothing else. Not a living thing: no birds in the air, no bears on the ice. Not a strip of land since Spitzbergen had sunk beneath the southern horizon. Not even a rock. A dead, dead world.

This then was the realm of Santa Claus. In the yearly Christmastide this ice field beneath us would be shrouded in the darkness of the six months' Arctic night. Perhaps the flaming aurora might

cast its fitful rays across the heavens for a few hours, or the milky beams of a pale midwinter moon cast blue-black shadows behind each up-ended floe. A million bright stars would sparkle in space. But the vast ice fields would remain empty and unmoving. In the sunless nights of the North the Christmas hours would silently file by.

A flash of all this came to me as I glanced through the window of my plane hurtling its way through space. How strange it seemed that a huge, black, useless, bitterly cold portion of the earth's surface should once a year become so important! And it *is* important when it bears upon the lives of boys and girls all over the world who believe there is a Santa Claus.

"But is there a Santa Claus?"

I have wondered since what Floyd Bennett, my pilot, would

have thought if I had written that question on our communication pad and handed it to him in the midst of our flight.

Then came the great moment. We were at the North Pole. Below us was nothing but ice. Ice spread to a clear horizon all around. Aged bergs huddled among the floes. Pressure ridges drifted deep with snow zigzagged across the white pack. Ugly scars over big floes showed where the tide had torn them apart, later to be healed by the bitter cold.

So this was the home of Santa Claus. This was the apex of the globe whence he sped southward each Christmas Eve to fill millions of stockings. This bleak icicled wilderness was the site of his renowned workshop. This was where he kept the record book of good deeds and bad against the names of little folk throughout the world. This was the fount of Christmas happiness from which flowed the sweetest wine of all the ages.

At least, so it was said. But was it true? Was there a Santa Claus?

I began to doubt it almost in the same breath. For trouble came. One engine looked as if it were going to die from an oil leak. Later my sextant, by which we were to navigate home, fell from the chart board and was broken. The other two engines might keep us up at a pinch. But if they did we might be lost owing to our inability to fix our position.

Brave Floyd Bennett shook his head. His optimism was dented by these two catastrophes. The fact we were prepared to march back over the ice did not help much. That was a desperate chance which we hoped we wouldn't be forced to take.

We swung about and set our compass course for home. But we could not tell if we were being forced adrift by the wind. We could not be sure at what moment the leaking oil would cause us to drop upon the wild and ragged ice below.

Yet we were too near the breaking point to feel real fear. For thirty-six hours before the hop-off we had not slept. We had now been in the air for many more hours. Nervous strain of the flight had told heavily on our strength.

In a sort of fitful petulance I thought back again to the comfort and safety of home. A curious flash of anger swept over me when the picture of my children came into my mind. I meant so much to their future. And here I was dangling on the brink of death.

I glanced at Bennett. His face told the story of his forebodings. He threw a look at the wrecked sextant and shook his head. I read his thought: Could we find our way without navigating? It was a gamble, all right.

I set my teeth. How could there be any Santa Claus in a world so cruel? The little faith I had had was slipping away. I could almost see the future. We should slither down on the jagged ice floes. We could not help wrecking the plane. We should crawl out and start the long trek home. Greenland, far west, was our only hope of escape. For months we should stagger onward through the snow and the bitter winds. We should die by inches.

What could my Lady tell the youngsters? Their Daddy had gone to the land of Santa Claus. He had never returned. The very thought made me shudder.

Time passed. We ought to sight land by now. But there was no land. I was right; Bennett was right. We had failed even though we had reached the Pole.

Suddenly my straining eyes caught a shadow on the horizon. A low curving cloud-like form stood there in the south. It couldn't be a cloud. Then I knew: It was land! We were saved! I should get back home. Little else mattered. What should I tell them? What would any man tell them after skimming so close to the end as had I?

"There is a Santa Claus! I know it for I have been to the Pole and seen!"

A Christmas in Brazil

By Kenneth Irving Brown

THERE are times when a man yearns for his home and the companionship of his friends. I had reached such a state of mind after four months in South America in search of flora for my botanical museum.

I lay back in the native dugout, lost in pleasant thoughts of home and a land where Nature was tamed. Pedro, a native Carib guide, between the lazy strokes of his paddle, had told me, in a lingo of distorted English and incomprehensible Spanish, of Cispatia, a tiny Carib town inland on the Mulatto River which he knew, of the villagers' "heart warmness," and of their isolation. If I understood him correctly, no white man had visited them for twenty years.

"And this is the day before Christmas," I mused. "We shall spend Christmas Eve at Cispatia; I shall be their Christmas guest." The thought was ironical, and I smiled bitterly.

It was approaching twilight when the village came into view. It consisted of a score of small huts with novel grass roofs, many of them built on sticks for protection against the attack of wild animals. An old man espied us and stood as if rooted to the spot, staring intently at us. Then with a wild shout, such as I have never heard, he cried: *"Hombres, hombres! Venid!"* and straightway running from the huts came men and women. They stopped abruptly when they saw us: with one accord they fell upon their knees and bowed their faces in the dust, all the while making a rhythmic moan, strangely beautiful.

I knew not what to make of this strange performance and my guide offered no information. As I stepped ashore, not a person stood, nor even peered at me through half-closed eyes; evidently that which I had taken for a moan was a prayer.

"Tell them we want to spend the night here," I said to my guide. No sooner had he spoken than they rushed toward me. In

no human eye have I ever seen expressed such emotion as was
written in theirs. Their eyes scanned my face with a hunger and
avidity quite disconcerting. When I raised my eyes to them to
signify that I would be their friend, they fell at my feet; they
even kissed my sandals. The entire performance was incomprehensible to me. Amazement at the presence of a white man hardly
accounted for their apparent worship. Presently I strolled down
to the bank of the stream and sat in wonder, while the shadows
of twilight thickened.

I could see the *hombres* and *mujeres* in the distance. They were
talking in soft tones. Suddenly one of the *muchachas*, young and
slender, came toward me. She walked with difficulty, leaning
heavily upon a staff at each step. Apparently her left side was
paralyzed. Her foot dragged as a leaden weight, and her arm
hung useless. No one moved among the group in the background,
and yet I could see they were watching her intently. The young
girl was trembling violently. I rose, wondering what was expected
of me, and even as I did she stumbled. Her staff fell from her
hand and she pitched forward. I caught her easily, and held her
trembling body for a moment. Then, with a cry of ecstasy, the
young thing leaped from my arms and flew back to the shadows.

As if waiting for this moment, her friends raised their voices with hers and there arose a solemn chanting, crude, yet beautiful in its sincerity and resplendent in its recurring note of joy. I longed to know the secret of the mystery.

The *muchacha's* staff lay at my feet. Could it be that these poor people, hearing of our progress in medicine, believed in the white man's miraculous power to heal? Faith is the ability to believe the incredible, I had heard it said.

I was so astonished at what had taken place, and so disconcerted by the plaintive chanting, that I hurried to the old father and made signs that I would retire. He understood and led me to the largest hut, where they had prepared a spreading of fresh palm-leaves with a blanket covering—the choicest sleeping-accommodation the camp offered, I knew—and I accepted with a gracious heart.

It was dawn when I awoke. Christmas Day—and yet how unbelievable. What was Christmas Day in a land of wilderness and black folk? What could it mean to these Carib Indians? It was with a feeling of wretchedness that I recalled past Christmases.

The dream was dispelled as I became aware of the voices which had awakened me, yet they stirred something within me which quieted the loneliness of my heart. There about the hut were gathered the inhabitants of the camp, with their arms laden. At sight of me they bowed themselves to the ground; then slowly one by one they came and laid their offerings at my feet. I stood as a man in a dream. At the foot of my ladder were heaped great skins of tiger and lynx, bananas, curiously carved images, and a reed basket woven in intricate design.

I did my best to express my thanks by smiles and gestures, but my confusion was turning to puzzled incredulity. I wanted to question my guide. They brought me food; and when I had eaten I sought my guide. "Pedro," I said, "we must away, at once."

He went to my host with word that we were going. The old man hurried to my side and through Pedro and pantomime begged me to stay. Then, seeing I was resolute, he motioned me to remain for a moment while he called the villagers together. Grouping themselves about me, they fell on their knees. By frantic gesticulation my host endeavored to communicate an idea to me. "Bless," said Pedro. They wanted me to bless them. I, an old, homesick, botany professor! I lifted my hands and repeated the words: "The Lord watch between me and thee, when we are absent one from another." Then, turning to my companion, I entered the dugout and we pushed off.

"Pedro, what did it all mean?"

He looked at me with eyes filled with amazement and doubt. "You know."

"I don't know; tell me." He hesitated; but at last he spoke.

"Christ come." No white man ever uttered such words with deeper reverence.

"Christ come!" I echoed, as I remembered their greeting and the incident of the night before.

"Yes, old miss'nary tell—Christ come. He come day 'fore Christmas; come up river at shade-time in dugout with *hombre*. He stay all night at Cispatia. They know at Cispatia."

I sat stunned by the thought. This then was the reason for their reception and their gifts; this the reason for the *muchacha's* confidence.

It was an idea which made me tremble. How inconceivable their childish faith, how perfect their adoration!

The canoe moved on. In the distance I heard music. It was the solemn chant they had sung for me when I came; they were singing it again as I left them.

Pedro leaned toward me. "It is true, *no es verdad?* You are, you are—He?"

The Inexhaustibility of the Subject of Christmas

By Leigh Hunt

SO MANY things have been said of late years about Christmas, that it is supposed by some there is no saying more. Oh, they of little faith! What? do they suppose that everything has been said that *can* be said, about any one Christmas thing?

About beef, for instance?

About plum-pudding?

About mince-pie?

About holly?

About ivy?

About rosemary?

About mistletoe? (Good God! what an immense number of things remain to be said about mistletoe!)

About Christmas Eve?

About hunt-the-slipper?

About hot cockles?

About blind-man's-buff?

About shoeing-the-wild-mare?

About thread-the-needle?

About he-can-do-little-that-can't-do-this?

About puss-in-the-corner?

About snapdragon?

About forfeits?

About Miss Smith?

About the bell-man?

About the waits?

About chilblains?

About carols?

About the fire?

About the block on it?

About schoolboys?

About their mothers?

About Christmas boxes?

About turkeys?

About Hogmany?

About goose-pie?

About mumming?

About saluting the apple-trees?

About brawn?

About plum-porridge?

About hobby-horse?

About hoppings?

About wakes?

About "feed-the-dove"?

About hackins?

About Yule doughs?

About going-a-gooding?

About loaf-stealing?

About julklaps? (Who has exhausted that subject, we should like to know?)

About wad-shooting?

About elder wine?

About pantomimes?

About cards?

About New-Year's day?

About gifts?

About wassail?

About twelfth-cake?

About king and queen?

About characters?

About eating too much?

About aldermen?

About the doctor?

About all being in the wrong?

About charity?

About all being in the right?

About Faith, Hope, and Endeavour?

About the Greatest Plum-pudding for the Greatest Number?

Esto perpetua; that is, Faith, Hope, and Charity, and Endeavour; and plum-pudding enough, by-and-by, all the year round, for everybody that likes it. Why that should not be the case, we cannot see—seeing that the earth is big, and human kind teachable, and God very good, and inciting us to do it.—Meantime, gravity apart, we ask anybody whether any of the above subjects are exhausted; and we inform everybody that all the above customs still exist in some parts of our beloved country, however unintelligible they may have become in others.—But to give a specimen of the non-exhaustion of any one of their topics.

Beef, for example. Now we should like to know who has exhausted the subject of the fine old roast Christmas piece of beef—from its original appearance in the meadows as part of the noble sultan of the herd, glorious old Taurus, the lord of the sturdy brow and ponderous agility, a sort of thunderbolt of a beast, well chosen by Jove to disguise in, one of Nature's most striking compounds of apparent heaviness and unencumbered activity—up to its contribution to the noble Christmas dinner, smoking from the spit, and flanked by the outposts of Bacchus.

Then plum-pudding! What a word is that! how plump, and plump again! How round, and repeated, and plenipotential! (There are two *p's*, observe, in plenipotential, and so there are in plum-pudding. We love an exquisite fitness—a might and wealth of adaptation.) Why, the whole round cheek of universal childhood is in the idea of plum-pudding; ay, and the weight of manhood, and the plentitude of the majesty of city dames. Wealth itself is symbolised by the least of its fruity particles. "A plum" is a city fortune—a million of money. He (the old boy, who has earned it)

> *Puts in his thumb,*

videlicet, into his pocket,

> *And pulls out a plum,*
> *And says what a "good man" am I.*

Observe a little boy at a Christmas dinner, and his grandfather opposite him. What a world of secret similarity there is between them. How hope in one, and retrospection in the other, and appetite in both, meet over the same ground of pudding, and understand it to a nicety. How the senior banters the little boy on his third slice; and how the little boy thinks within himself that he dines that day as well as the senior. How both look hot, and red, and smiling, and juvenile. How the little boy is conscious of the Christmas box in his pocket (of which indeed the grandfather jocosely puts him in mind); and how the grandfather is quite as conscious of the plum, or part of a plum, or whatever fraction it may be, in his own. How he incites the little boy to love money and good dinners all his life; and how determined the little boy is to abide by his advice,—with a secret addition in favour of holidays and marbles—to which there is an analogy, in the senior's mind, on the side of trips to Hastings, and a game at whist. Finally, the old gentleman sees his own face in the pretty smooth one of the child; and if the child is not best pleased at his proclamation of the likeness (in truth, is horrified at it, and thinks it a sort of madness,) yet nice observers, who have lived long enough to see the wonderful changes in people's faces from youth to age, probably discern the thing well enough; and feel a movement of pathos at their hearts, in considering the world of trouble and emotion that is the causer of the changes. *That* old man's face was once like that little boy's! *That* little boy's will be one day like that old man's! What a thought to make us all love and respect one another, if not for our fine qualities, yet, at least, for the trouble and sorrow which we all go through!

Ay, and joy too! for all people have their joys as well as troubles, at one time or another; most likely both together, or in constant alternation; and the greater part of troubles are not the worst things in the world, but only graver forms of the requisite motion of the universe, or workings towards a better condition of things, the greater or less violent according as we give them violence for violence, or respect them like awful but not ill-meaning gods, and entertain them with a rewarded patience.—Grave thoughts, you will say, for Christmas. But no season has a greater right to grave thoughts, in passing; and for that very reason, no season has a greater right to let them pass, and recur to more light ones.

So a noble and merry season to you, my masters; and may we meet, thick and threefold, many a time and oft in blithe yet most thoughtful pages. Fail not to call in mind, in the course of the 25th of this month, that the Divinest Heart that ever walked the earth was born on that day, and then smile and enjoy yourselves for the rest of it, for mirth is also of heaven's making, and wondrous was the wine-drinking at Galilee.

The Peterkins' Christmas Tree

By Lucretia P. Hale

EARLY in the autumn the Peterkins began to prepare for their Christmas tree. Everything was done in great privacy, as it was to be a surprise to the neighbors, as well as to the rest of the family. Mr. Peterkin had been up to Mr. Bromwick's wood-lot, and, with his consent, selected the tree. Agamemnon went to look at it occasionally after dark, and Solomon John made frequent visits to it mornings, just after sunrise. Mr. Peterkin drove Elizabeth Eliza and her mother that way, and pointed furtively to it with his whip; but none of them ever spoke of it aloud to each other. It was suspected that the little boys had been to see it Wednesday and Saturday afternoons. But they came home with their pockets full of chestnuts, and said nothing about it.

At length Mr. Peterkin had it cut down and brought secretly into the Larkins' barn. A week or two before Christmas a measurement was made of it with Elizabeth Eliza's yard-measure. To Mr. Peterkin's great dismay it was discovered that it was too high to stand in the back parlor.

This fact was brought out at a secret council of Mr. and Mrs. Peterkin, Elizabeth Eliza, and Agamemnon.

Agamemnon suggested that it might be set up slanting; but Mrs. Peterkin was very sure it would make her dizzy, and the candles would drip.

But a brilliant idea came to Mr. Peterkin. He proposed that the ceiling of the parlor should be raised to make room for the top of the tree.

Elizabeth Eliza thought the space would need to be quite large. It must not be like a small box, or you could not see the tree.

"Yes," said Mr. Peterkin, "I should have the ceiling lifted all across the room; the effect would be finer."

Elizabeth Eliza objected to having the whole ceiling raised, because her room was over the back parlor, and she would have

36

no floor while the alteration was going on, which would be very awkward. Besides, her room was not very high now, and, if the floor were raised, perhaps she could not walk in it upright.

Mr. Peterkin explained that he didn't propose altering the whole ceiling, but to lift up a ridge across the room at the back part where the tree was to stand. This would make a hump, to be sure, in Elizabeth Eliza's room; but it would go across the whole room.

Elizabeth Eliza said she would not mind that. It would be like the cuddy thing that comes up on the deck of a ship, that you sit against, only here you would not have the seasickness. She thought she should like it, for a rarity. She might use it for a divan.

Mrs. Peterkin thought it would come in the worn place of the carpet, and might be a convenience in making the carpet over.

Agamemnon was afraid there would be trouble in keeping the matter secret, for it would be a long piece of work for a carpenter; but Mr. Peterkin proposed having the carpenter for a day or two, for a number of other jobs.

One of them was to make all the chairs in the house of the same height, for Mrs. Peterkin had nearly broken her spine by sitting down in a chair that she had supposed was her own rocking-chair, and it had proved to be two inches lower. The little boys were now large enough to sit in any chair; so a medium was fixed upon to satisfy all the family, and the chairs were made uniformly of the same height.

On consulting the carpenter, however, he insisted that the tree could be cut off at the lower end to suit the height of the parlor, and demurred at so great change as altering the ceiling. But Mr. Peterkin had set his mind upon the improvement, and Elizabeth Eliza had cut her carpet in preparation for it.

So the folding-doors into the back parlor were closed, and for nearly a fortnight before Christmas there was great litter of fallen plastering, and laths, and chips, and shavings; and Elizabeth Eliza's carpet was taken up, and the furniture had to be changed, and one night she had to sleep at the Bromwicks', for there was a long hole in her floor that might be dangerous.

All this delighted the little boys. They could not understand what was going on. Perhaps they suspected a Christmas tree, but they did not know why a Christmas tree should have so many chips, and were still more astonished at the hump that appeared in Elizabeth Eliza's room. It must be a Christmas present, or else the tree in a box.

Some aunts and uncles, too, arrived a day or two before Christmas, with some small cousins. These cousins occupied the attention of the little boys, and there was a great deal of whispering and mystery, behind doors, and under the stairs, and in the corners of the entry.

Solomon John was busy, privately making some candles for the tree. He had been collecting some bayberries, as he understood they made very nice candles, so that it would not be necessary to buy any.

The elders of the family never all went into the back parlor together, and all tried not to see what was going on. Mr. Peterkin would go in with Solomon John, or Mr. Peterkin with Elizabeth Eliza, or Elizabeth Eliza and Agamemnon and Solomon John. The little boys and the small cousins were never allowed even to look inside the room.

Elizabeth Eliza meanwhile went into town a number of times. She wanted to consult Amanda as to how much ice-cream they should need, and whether they could make it at home, as they had cream and ice. She was pretty busy in her own room; the furniture had to be changed, and the carpet altered. The "hump" was higher than she expected. There was danger of bumping her own head whenever she crossed it. She had to nail some padding on the ceiling for fear of accidents.

The afternoon before Christmas, Elizabeth Eliza, Solomon John, and their father collected in the back parlor for a council. The carpenters had done their work, and the tree stood at its full height at the back of the room, the top stretching up into the space arranged for it. All the chips and shavings were cleared away, and it stood on a neat box.

But what were they to put upon the tree?

Solomon John had brought in his supply of candles; but they proved to be very "stringy" and very few of them. It was strange how many bayberries it took to make a few candles! The little boys had helped him, and he had gathered as much as a bushel of bayberries. He had put them in water, and skimmed off the wax, according to the directions; but there was so little wax!

Solomon John had given the little boys some of the bits sawed off from the legs of the chairs. He had suggested that they should cover them with gilt paper, to answer for gilt apples, without telling them what they were for.

These apples, a little blunt at the end, and the candles, were all they had for the tree!

After all her trips into town Elizabeth Eliza had forgotten to bring anything for it.

"I thought of candies and sugar-plums," she said; "but I concluded if we made caramels ourselves we should not need them. But, then, we have not made caramels. The fact is, that day my head was full of my carpet. I had bumped it pretty badly, too."

Mr. Peterkin wished he had taken, instead of a fir-tree, an apple-tree he had seen in October, full of red fruit.

"But the leaves would have fallen off by this time," said Elizabeth Eliza.

"And the apples, too," said Solomon John.

"It is odd I should have forgotten, that day I went in on purpose to get the things," said Elizabeth Eliza, musingly. "But I went from shop to shop, and didn't know exactly what to get. I saw a great many gilt things for Christmas-trees; but I knew the little boys were making the gilt apples; there were plenty of candles in the shops, but I knew Solomon John was making the candles."

Mr. Peterkin thought it was quite natural.

Solomon John wondered if it were too late for them to go into town now.

Elizabeth Eliza could not go in the next morning, for there was to be a grand Christmas dinner, and Mr. Peterkin could not be spared, and Solomon John was sure he and Agamemnon would not know what to buy. Besides, they would want to try the candles tonight.

Mr. Peterkin asked if the presents everybody had been preparing would not answer. But Elizabeth Eliza knew they would be too heavy.

A gloom came over the room. There was only a flickering gleam from one of Solomon John's candles that he had lighted by way of trial.

Solomon John again proposed going into town. He lighted a

match to examine the newspaper about the trains. There were plenty of trains coming out at that hour, but none going in except a very late one. That would not leave time to do anything and come back.

"We could go in, Elizabeth Eliza and I," said Solomon John, "but we should not have time to buy anything."

Agamemnon was summoned in. Mrs. Peterkin was entertaining the uncles and aunts in the front parlor. Agamemnon wished there was time to study up something about electric lights. If they could only have a calcium light! Solomon John's candle sputtered and went out.

At this moment there was a loud knocking at the front door. The little boys, and the small cousins, and the uncles and aunts, and Mrs. Peterkin, hastened to see what was the matter.

The uncles and aunts thought somebody's house must be on fire. The door was opened, and there was a man, white with flakes, for it was beginning to snow, and he was pulling in a large box.

Mrs. Peterkin supposed it contained some of Elizabeth Eliza's purchases, so she ordered it to be pushed into the back parlor, and hastily called back her guests and the little boys into the other room. The little boys and the small cousins were sure they had seen Santa Claus himself.

Mr. Peterkin lighted the gas. The box was addressed to Elizabeth Eliza. It was from the lady from Philadelphia! She had gathered a hint from Elizabeth Eliza's letters that there was to be a Christmas tree, and had filled this box with all that would be needed.

It was opened directly. There was every kind of gilt hanging-thing, from gilt pea-pods to butterflies on springs. There were shining flags and lanterns, and bird-cages, and nests with birds sitting on them, baskets of fruit, gilt apples and bunches of grapes, and, at the bottom of the whole, a large box of candles and a box of Philadelphia bonbons!

Elizabeth Eliza and Solomon John could scarcely keep from screaming. The little boys and the small cousins knocked on the folding-doors to ask what was the matter.

Hastily Mr. Peterkin and the rest took out the things and hung them on the tree, and put on the candles.

When all was done, it looked so well that Mr. Peterkin exclaimed:

"Let us light the candles now, and send to invite all the neighbors tonight, and have the tree on Christmas Eve!"

And so it was that the Peterkins had their Christmas tree the day before, and on Christmas night could go and visit their neighbors.

Christmas Day in Old England

By WASHINGTON IRVING

WHEN I woke on Christmas morning, I heard the sound of little feet pattering outside of the door, and a whispering consultation. Presently a choir of small voices chanted forth an old Christmas carol, the burden of which was—

> *"Rejoice, our Saviour he was born*
> *On Christmas day in the morning."*

I rose softly, slipt on my clothes, opened the door suddenly, and beheld one of the most beautiful little fairy groups that a painter could imagine. It consisted of a boy and two girls, the eldest not more than six, and lovely as seraphs. They were going the rounds of the house, and singing at every chamber door; but my sudden appearance frightened them into mute bashfulness. They remained for a moment playing on their lips with their fingers, and now and then stealing a shy glance, from under their eyebrows, until, as if by one impulse, they scampered away, and as they turned an angle of the gallery, I heard them laughing in triumph at their escape.

After breakfast I was told that the squire was a little particular in having his household at church on a Christmas morning; considering it a day of pouring out of thanks and rejoicing; for, as old Tusser observed,

"At Christmas be merry, and thankful withal,
  And feast thy poor neighbors, the great with the small."

On reaching the church porch, we found the parson rebuking the gray-headed sexton for having used mistletoe among the greens with which the church was decorated. It was, he observed, an unholy plant, profaned by having been used by the Druids in their mystic ceremonies; and though it might be innocently employed in the festive ornamenting of halls and kitchens, yet it had been deemed by the Fathers of the Church as unhallowed, and totally unfit for sacred purposes. So tenacious was he on this point, that the poor sexton was obliged to strip down a great part of the humble trophies of his taste, before the parson would consent to enter upon the service of the day.

The parson gave us a most erudite sermon on the rites and ceremonies of Christmas, and the propriety of observing it not merely as a day of thanksgiving, but of rejoicing; supporting the correctness of his opinions by the earliest usages of the church, and enforcing them by the authorities of Theophilus of Cesarea, St. Cyprian, St. Chrysostom, St. Augustine, and a cloud more of saints and fathers, from whom he made copious quotations. I was a little at a loss to perceive the necessity of such a mighty array of forces to maintain a point which no one present seemed inclined to dispute; but I soon found that the good man had a legion of ideal adversaries to contend with; having, in the course of his researches on the subject of Christmas, got completely embroiled in the sectarian controversies of the Revolution, when the Puritans made such a fierce assault upon the ceremonies of the church, and poor old Christmas was driven out of the land by proclamation of Parliament. The worthy parson lived but with times past, and knew but little of the present.

Shut up among worm-eaten tomes in the retirement of his antiquated little study, the pages of old times were to him as the

gazettes of the day; while the era of the Revolution was mere
modern history. He forgot that nearly two centuries had elapsed
since the fiery persecution of poor mince-pie throughout the land;
when plum porridge was denounced as "mere popery," and roast
beef as anti-Christian; and that Christmas had been brought in
again triumphantly with the merry court of King Charles at the
Restoration.

I have seldom known a sermon attended apparently with more
immediate effects; for on leaving the church the congregation
seemed one and all possessed with the gayety of spirit so earnestly
enjoined by their pastor. The elder folks gathered in knots in the
church-yard, greeting and shaking hands; and the children ran
about crying Ule! Ule! and repeating some uncouth rhymes,

> "Ule! Ule!
> Three puddings in a pule;
> Crack nuts and cry ule!"

which the parson, who had joined us, informed me had been
handed down from days of yore. The villagers doffed their hats
to the squire as he passed, giving him the good wishes of the
season with every appearance of heartfelt sincerity, and were
invited by him to the hall, to take something to keep out the cold
of the weather; and I heard blessings uttered by several of the
poor, which convinced me that, in the midst of his enjoyments,
the worthy old cavalier had not forgotten the true Christmas
virtue of charity.

We had not been long home when the sound of music was
heard from a distance. A band of country lads, without coats,
their shirt sleeves fancifully tied with ribands, their hats decorated with greens, and clubs in their hands, was seen advancing
up the avenue, followed by a large number of villagers and peas-
antry. They stopped before the hall door, where the music struck
up a peculiar air, and the lads performed a curious and intricate
dance, advancing, retreating, and striking their clubs together,
keeping exact time to the music; while one, whimsically crowned
with a fox's skin, the tail of which flaunted down his back, kept
capering round the skirts of the dance, and rattling a Christmas
box with many antic gesticulations.

The squire eyed this fanciful exhibition with great interest and delight, and gave me a full account of its origin, which he traced to the times when the Romans held possession of the island; plainly proving that this was a lineal descendant of the sword dance of the ancients. "It was now," he said, "nearly extinct, but he had accidentally met with traces of it in the neighborhood, and had encouraged its revival; though, to tell the truth, it was too apt to be followed up by the rough cudgel play, and broken heads in the evening."

After the dance was concluded, the whole party was entertained with brawn and beef, and stout home-brewed. The squire himself mingled among the rustics, and was received with awkward demonstrations of deference and regard.

The whole house indeed seemed abandoned to merriment: as I passed to my room to dress for dinner, I heard the sound of music in a small court, and looking through a window that commanded it, I perceived a band of wandering musicians, with pandean pipes and tambourine; a pretty coquettish housemaid was dancing a jig with a smart country lad, while several of the other servants were looking on. In the midst of her sport the girl caught a glimpse of my face at the window, and, coloring up, ran off with an air of roguish affected confusion.

The dinner was served up in the great hall, where the squire always held his Christmas banquet. A blazing crackling fire of logs had been heaped on to warm the spacious apartment, and the flame went sparkling and wreathing up the wide-mouthed chimney. The great picture of the crusader and his white horse had been profusely decorated with greens for the occasion; and holly and ivy had likewise been wreathed round the helmet and weapons on the opposite wall, which I understood were the arms of the same warrior.

We were ushered into this banqueting scene with the sound of minstrelsy, the old harper being seated on a stool beside the fireplace, and twanging his instrument with a vast deal more power than melody. Never did Christmas board display a more goodly and gracious assemblage of countenances; those who were not handsome were, at least, happy; and happiness is a rare improver of your hard-favored visage.

The parson said grace, which was not a short familiar one, such as is commonly addressed to the Deity in these unceremonious days; but a long, courtly, well-worded one of the ancient school. There was now a pause, as if something was expected; when suddenly the butler entered the hall with some degree of bustle: he was attended by a servant on each side with a large wax-light, and bore a silver dish, on which was an enormous pig's head, decorated with rosemary, with a lemon in its mouth, which was placed with great formality at the head of the table. The moment this pageant made its appearance, the harper struck up a flourish;

at the conclusion of which the young Oxonian, on receiving a hint from the squire, gave, with an air of the most comic gravity, an old carol, the first verse of which was as follows:

> *Caput apri defero*
> *Reddens laudes Domino.*
> *The boar's head in hand bring I,*
> *With garlands gay and rosemary.*
> *I pray you all synge merily*
> *Qui estis in convivio.*

Though prepared to witness many of these little eccentricities, from being apprised of the peculiar hobby of mine host; yet, I confess, the parade with which so odd a dish was introduced somewhat perplexed me, until I gathered from the conversation of the squire and the parson, that it was meant to represent the bringing in of the boar's head; a dish formerly served up with much ceremony and the sound of minstrelsy and song, at great tables, on Christmas day. "I like the old custom," said the squire, "not merely because it is stately and pleasing in itself, but because it was observed at the college at Oxford at which I was educated. When I hear the old song chanted, it brings to mind the time when I was young and gamesome—and the noble old college hall —and my fellow students loitering about in their black gowns; many of whom, poor lads, are now in their graves!"

The parson, however, whose mind was not haunted by such associations, and who was always more taken up with the text than the sentiment, objected to the Oxonian's version of the carol; which he affirmed was different from that sung at college. He went on, with the dry perseverance of a commentator, to give the college reading, accompanied by sundry annotations; addressing himself at first to the company at large; but finding their attention gradually diverted to other talk and other objects, he lowered his tone as his number of auditors diminished, until he concluded his remarks in an under voice, to a fat-headed old gentleman next him, who was silently engaged in the discussion of a huge plateful of turkey.

The table was literally loaded with good cheer, and presented an epitome of country abundance, in this season of overflowing larders. A distinguished post was allotted to "ancient sirloin," as mine host termed it; being, as he added, "the standard of old English hospitality, and a joint of goodly presence, and full of expectation." There were several dishes quaintly decorated, and which had evidently something traditional in their embellishments; but about which, as I did not like to appear over-curious, I asked no questions.

I could not, however, but notice a pie, magnificently decorated with peacock's feathers, in imitation of the tail of that bird, which overshadowed a considerable tract of the table. This, the squire confessed, with some little hesitation, was a pheasant pie, though a peacock pie was certainly the most authentical; but there had been such a mortality among the peacocks this season, that he could not prevail upon himself to have one killed.

It would be tedious, perhaps, to my wiser readers, who may not have that foolish fondness for odd and obsolete things to which I am a little given, were I to mention the other makeshifts of this worthy old humorist, by which he was endeavoring to follow up, though at humble distance, the quaint customs of antiquity. I was pleased, however, to see the respect shown to his whims by his children and relatives; who, indeed, entered readily into the full spirit of them, and seemed all well versed in their parts; having doubtless been present at many a rehearsal. I was amused, too, at the air of profound gravity with which the butler and other servants executed the duties assigned them, however eccentric. They had an old-fashioned look; having, for the most part, been brought up in the household, and grown into keeping with the antiquated mansion, and the humors of its lord; and most probably looked upon all his whimsical regulations as the established laws of honorable housekeeping.

When the cloth was removed, the butler brought in a huge silver vessel of rare and curious workmanship, which he placed before the squire. Its appearance was hailed with acclamation; being the Wassail Bowl, so renowned in Christmas festivity. The contents had been prepared by the squire himself; for it was a beverage in the skillful mixture of which he particularly prided himself: alleging that it was too abstruse and complex for the comprehension of an ordinary servant. It was a potation, indeed, that might well make the heart of a toper leap within him; being composed of the richest and raciest wines, highly spiced and sweetened, with roasted apples bobbing about the surface.

The old gentleman's whole countenance beamed with a serene look of indwelling delight as he stirred this mighty bowl. Having raised it to his lips, with a hearty wish of a merry Christmas to all present, he sent it brimming round the board, for every one to follow his example, according to the primitive style; pronouncing it "the ancient fountain of good feeling, where all hearts met together."

December 25th, 1914

A Letter from the Western Front, written by Sir Edward Hamilton Westrow Hulse, Bart., *killed in action March 25th, 1915, at the age of twenty-five years*

My Dearest Mother,

Just returned to billets again, after the most extraordinary Christmas in the trenches you could possibly imagine.

On the 23rd we took over the trenches in the ordinary manner, relieving the Grenadiers, and during the 24th the usual

firing took place, and sniping was pretty brisk. We stood to arms as usual at 6.30 on the 25th, and I noticed that there was not much shooting; this gradually died down, and by 8 A.M. there was no shooting at all, except for a few shots on our left (Border Regt.). At 8.30 A.M. I was looking out, and saw four Germans leave their trenches and come towards us; I told two of my men to go and meet them, unarmed (as the Germans were unarmed) and to see that they did not pass the half-way line. We were 350-

49

400 yards apart at this point. My fellows were not very keen, not knowing what was up. So I went out alone and met Barry, one of our ensigns, also coming out from another part of the line. By the time we got to them, they were three-quarters of the way over, and much too near our barbed wire, so I moved them back. They were three private soldiers and a stretcher-bearer, and their spokesman started off by saying that he thought it only right to come over and wish us a happy Christmas, and trusted us implicitly to keep the truce. He came from Suffolk, where he had left his best girl and a 3½ h.p. motor bike! He told me that he could not get a letter to the girl, and wanted to send one through me. I made him write out a letter in front of me in English and I sent it off that night. I told him that she probably would not be a bit keen to see him again. We then entered a long discussion on every sort of thing. I was dressed in an old stocking-cap and a men's overcoat, and they took me for a corporal, a thing which I did not discourage, as I had an eye to going as near their lines as possible. . . . I asked them what orders they had from their officers as to coming over to us, and they said none; they had just come over.

They protested that they had no feeling of enmity towards us at all, but that everything lay with their authorities, and that being soldiers they had to obey. I believe that they were speaking the truth when they said this, and that they never wished to fire a shot again. They said that, unless directly ordered, they were not going to shoot again until we did. . . . We talked about the ghastly wounds made by rifle bullets, and we both agreed that neither of us used dum-dum bullets, and that the wounds are solely inflicted by the high-velocity bullet with the sharp nose, at short range. We both agreed that it would be far better if we used the old South African round-nosed bullet, which makes a clean hole. . . .

They think that our Press is to blame in working up feeling against them by publishing false "atrocity reports." I told them of various sweet little cases which I have seen for myself. And they told me of English prisoners whom they have seen with soft-nosed bullets, and lead bullets with notches cut in the nose; we had a heated and at the same time good-natured argument, and ended by hinting to each other that the other was lying!

I kept it up for half an hour, and then escorted them back as far as their barbed wire, having a jolly good look round all the time, and picking up various little bits of information which I had not had an opportunity of doing under fire! I left instructions with them that if any of them came out later they must not come over the half-way line, and appointed a ditch as the meeting-place. We parted after an exchange of Albany cigarettes and German cigars, and I went straight to Headquarters to report.

A German N.C.O. with the Iron Cross—gained, he told me, for conspicuous skill in sniping—started his fellows off on some marching tune. When they had done I set the note for "The Boys of Bonnie Scotland, where the heather and the bluebells grow," and so we went on, singing everything from "Good King Wenceslaus" down to the ordinary Tommies' song, and ended up with "Auld Lang Syne," which we all, English, Scots, Irish, Prussian, Württembergers, etc., joined it. It was absolutely astounding, and if I had seen it on a film should have sworn that it was faked! . . .

During the afternoon the same extraordinary scene was enacted between the lines, and one of the enemy told me that he was longing to get back to London: I assured him that "So was I." He said that he was sick of the war, and I told him that when the truce was ended any of his friends would be welcome in our trenches, and would be well received, fed, and given a free passage to the Isle of Man! At 4.30 P.M. we agreed to keep in our respective trenches, and told them that the truce was ended. They persisted, however, in saying that they were not going to fire, and as George had told us not to unless they did, we prepared for a quiet night, but warned all sentries to be doubly on the alert.

During the day both sides had taken the opportunity of bringing up piles of wood, and straw, etc., which is generally only brought up with difficulty under fire. We improved our dugouts, roofed in new ones and got a lot of very useful work done towards increasing our comfort. Directly it was dark, I got the whole of my Company on to improving and re-making our barbed-wire entanglements, all along my front, and had my scouts out in front of the working parties, to prevent any surprises; but not a shot was fired, and we finished off a real good obstacle unmolested.

They apparently treated our prisoners well, and did all they could for our wounded. Their officer kept on pointing to our dead and saying, "*Les Braves, c'est bien dommage.*" . . .

When George had heard of it he went down to that section and talked to the nice officer and gave him a scarf. That same evening a German orderly came to the half-way line, and brought a pair of warm, woolly gloves as a present in return for George.

The same night the Borders and we were engaged in putting up big trestle obstacles, with barbed wire all over them and connecting them, and at this same point (namely, where we were only 85 yards apart) the Germans came out and sat on their parapet, and watched us doing it, although we had informed them that the truce was ended. Well, all was quiet, as I said, that night; and next morning, while I was having breakfast, one of my N.C.O.'s came and reported that the enemy were again coming over to talk. I had given full instructions, and none of my men were allowed out of the trenches to talk to the enemy. I had also told the N.C.O. of an advanced post which I have up a ditch, to go out with two men, unarmed; if any of the enemy came over, to see that they did not cross the half-way line, and to engage them in pleasant conversation. So I went out and found the same lot as the day before; they told me again that they had no intention of firing, and wished the truce to continue. I had instructions not to fire till the enemy did; I told them; and so the same comic form of temporary truce continued on the 26th, and again at 4.30 P.M. I informed them that the truce was at an end. We had sent them over some plum-puddings, and they thanked us heartily for them and retired again, the only difference being that instead of all my men being out in the "no man's zone," one N.C.O. and two men only were allowed out, and the enemy therefore sent fewer.

Again both sides had been improving their comfort during the day, and again at night I continued on my barbed-wire and finished it right off. We returned for the night all quiet, and were rudely awakened at 11 P.M. A Headquarters orderly burst into my dugout, and handed me a message. It stated that a deserter had come into the 8th Division lines, and stated that the whole German line was going to attack at 12:15 midnight, and that we were to stand to arms immediately, and that reinforcements were being hurried up from billets in rear. I thought, at the time, that it was a d——d good joke on the part of the German deserter to deprive us of our sleep, and so it turned out to be. I stood my Company to arms, made a few extra dispositions, gave out all instructions, and at 11.20 P.M. George arrived. . . . Suddenly our guns all along the line opened a heavy fire, and all the enemy did was to reply with 9 shell (heavy howitzers) not one of which exploded, just on my left. Never a rifle shot was fired by either side (except right away down in the 8th Division), and at 2.30 P.M. we turned in half the men to sleep, and kept half awake on sentry.

Apparently this deserter had also reported that strong German reinforcements had been brought up, and named a place just in rear of their lines, where, he said, two regiments were in billets that had just been brought up. Our guns were informed, and plastered the place well when they opened fire (as I mentioned). The long and short of it was that absolutely nothing happened, and after a sleepless night I turned in at 4.30 A.M. and was woken again at 6.30 when we always stand to arms before daylight.

I was just going to have another sleep at 8 A.M. when I found that the enemy were again coming over to talk to us (December 27th). I watched my N.C.O. and two men go out from the advanced post to meet them, and hearing shouts of laughter from the little party when they met, I again went out myself.

They asked me what we were up to during the night, and told me that they had stood to arms all night and thought we were going to attack them when they heard our heavy shelling; also that our guns had done a lot of damage and knocked out a lot of their men in billets. I told them a deserter of theirs had come over to us, and that they had only him to thank for the damage done, and that we, after a sleepless night, were not best pleased with him either! They assured me that they had heard nothing of an attack, and I fully believed them, as it is inconceivable that they would have allowed us to put up the formidable obstacles (which we had on the two previous nights) if they had contemplated an offensive movement.

Anyhow, if it had ever existed, the plan had miscarried, as no attack was developed on any part of our line, and here were these fellows still protesting that there was a truce, although I told them that it had ceased the evening before. So I kept to the same arrangement, namely, that my N.C.O. and two men should meet them half-way, and strict orders were given that no other man was to leave the lines. . . . I admit that the whole thing beat me absolutely.

In the evening we were relieved by the Grenadiers.

St. Nicholas' Eve in Hans Brinker's Day

By MARY MAPES DODGE

WE ALL know how, before the Christmas tree began to flourish in the home life of our country, a certain "right jolly old elf," with "eight tiny reindeer," used to drive his sleigh-load of toys up to our housetops, and then bound down the chimney to fill the stockings so hopefully hung by the fireplace. His friends called him Santa Claus; and those who were most intimate ventured to say, "Old Nick." It was said that he originally came from Holland. *Here* Santa Claus comes rollicking along on the 25th of December, our holy Christmas morn; but in Holland, St. Nicholas visits earth on the 5th, a time especially appropriated to him. Early on the morning of the 6th, which is St. Nicholas Day, he distributes his candies, toys, and treasures, then vanishes for a year.

Christmas Day is devoted by the Hollanders to church rites and pleasant family visiting. It is on St. Nicholas' Eve that their young people become half wild with joy and expectation. To some of them it is a sorry time, for the saint is very candid, and, if any of them have been bad during the past year, he is quite sure to tell them so. Sometimes he carries a birch rod under his arm, and advises the parents to give them scoldings in place of confections, and floggings instead of toys.

Hilda van Gleck's little brothers and sisters were in a high state of excitement that night. They had been admitted into the grand parlor: they were dressed in their best, and had been given two cakes apiece at supper. Hilda was as joyous as any. Why not? St. Nicholas would never cross a girl of fourteen from his list, just because she was tall and looked almost like a woman. On the contrary, he would probably exert himself to do honor to such an august-looking damsel. Who could tell? So she sported and laughed and danced as gayly as the youngest, and was the soul of all their merry games. Father, mother, and grandmother looked on approvingly: so did grandfather, before he spread his large red handkerchief over his face, leaving only the top of his skull-cap visible. This kerchief was his ensign of sleep.

Earlier in the evening, all had joined in the fun. In the general hilarity, there had seemed to be a difference only in bulk between grandfather and the baby. Indeed, a shade of solemn expectation, now and then flitting across the faces of the younger members, had made them seem rather more thoughtful than their elders.

Now the spirit of fun reigned supreme. The very flames danced and capered in the polished grate. A pair of prim candles, that had been staring at the astral lamp, began to wink at other candles far away in the mirrors. Passers-by halted to catch the merry laughter floating through curtain and sash, into the street, then skipped on their way with a startled consciousness that the village was wide awake. At last matters grew so uproarious, that the grandsire's red kerchief came down from his face with a jerk. What decent old gentleman could sleep in such a racket! Mynheer van Gleck regarded his children with astonishment. The baby even showed symptoms of hysterics. It was high time to attend to business. Mevrouw suggested that, if they wished to see the good St. Nicholas, they should sing the same loving invitation that had brought him the year before.

The baby stared, and thrust his fist into his mouth, as mynheer put him down upon the floor. Soon he sat erect, and looked with a sweet scowl at the company. With his lace and embroideries, and his crown of blue ribbon and whalebone (for he was not quite past the tumbling age), he looked like the king of the babies.

The other children, each holding a pretty willow basket, formed at once in a ring, and moved slowly around the little fellow, lifting their eyes meanwhile; for the saint to whom they were about to address themselves was yet in mysterious quarters.

Mevrouw commenced playing softly upon the piano: soon the voices rose,—gentle youthful voices, rendered all the sweeter for their tremor,—

"Welcome, friend! St. Nicholas, welcome!
Bring no rod for us tonight!
While our voices bid thee welcome,
Every heart with joy is light.

Tell us every fault and failing;
We will bear thy keenest railing.
So we sing, so we sing:
Thou shalt tell us everything!

Welcome, friend! St. Nicholas, welcome!
Welcome to this merry band!
Happy children greet thee, welcome!
Thou art gladdening all the land.

Fill each empty hand and basket;
'Tis thy little ones who ask it.
So we sing, so we sing:
Thou wilt bring us everything!"

During the chorus, sundry glances, half in eagerness, half in dread, had been cast towards the polished folding-doors. Now a loud knocking was heard. The circle was broken in an instant. Some little ones, with a strange mixture of fear and delight, pressed against their mother's knee. Grandfather bent forward, with his chin resting upon his hand; grandmother lifted her spectacles; mynheer van Gleck, seated by the fireplace, slowly drew his meerschaum from his mouth; while Hilda and the other children settled themselves beside him in an expectant group.

The knocking was heard again.

"Come in," said the mevrouw softly.

The door slowly opened; and St. Nicholas, in full array, stood before them. You could have heard a pin drop. Soon he spoke. What a mysterious majesty in his voice! What kindliness in his tones!

"Karel van Gleck, I am pleased to greet thee, and thy honored vrouw, Kathrine, and thy son, and his good vrouw, Annie.

"Children, I greet ye all—Hendrick, Hilda, Broom, Katy, Huygens, and Lucretia. And thy cousins—Wolfert, Diedrich,

Mayken, Voost, and Katrina. Good children ye have been, in the main, since I last accosted ye. Diedrich was rude at the Haarlem fair last fall; but he has tried to atone for it since. Mayken has failed, of late, in her lessons; and too many sweets and trifles have gone to her lips, and too few stivers to her charity-box. Diedrich, I trust, will be a polite, manly boy for the future; and Mayken will endeavor to shine as a student. Let her remember, too, that economy and thrift are needed in the foundation of a worthy and generous life. Little Katy has been cruel to the cat more than once. St. Nicholas can hear the cat cry when its tail is pulled. I will forgive her, if she will remember from this hour that the smallest dumb creatures have feeling, and must not be abused."

As Katy burst into a frightened cry, the saint graciously remained silent until she was soothed.

"Master Broom," he resumed, "I warn thee that boys who are in the habit of putting snuff upon the foot-stove of the school-mistress may one day be discovered, and receive a flogging ——"

(Master Broom colored, and stared in great astonishment.)

"But thou art such an excellent scholar, I shall make thee no further reproof.

"Thou, Hendrick, didst distinguish thyself in the archery match last spring, and hit the bull's-eye, though the bird was swung before it to unsteady thine eye. I give thee credit for excelling in manly sport and exercise; though I must not unduly countenance thy boat-racing, since it leaves thee too little time for thy proper studies.

"Lucretia and Hilda shall have a blessed sleep tonight. The consciousness of kindness to the poor, devotion in their souls, and cheerful, hearty obedience to household rule, will render them happy.

"With one and all I avow myself well content. Goodness, industry, benevolence, and thrift have prevailed in your midst. Therefore, my blessing upon you; and may the New Year find all treading the paths of obedience, wisdom, and love! Tomorrow you shall find more substantial proofs that I have been in your midst. Farewell!"

With these words came a great shower of sugarplums upon a linen sheet spread out in front of the doors. A general scramble followed. The children fairly tumbled over each other in their eagerness to fill their baskets. Mevrouw cautiously held the baby down in their midst till the chubby little fists were filled. Then the bravest of the youngsters sprang up and burst open the closed doors. In vain they peered into the mysterious department. St. Nicholas was nowhere to be seen.

Soon there was a general rush to another room, where stood a table, covered with the finest and whitest of linen damask. Each child, in a flutter of excitement, laid a shoe upon it. The door was then carefully locked, and its key hidden in the mother's bedroom. Next followed good-night kisses, a grand family procession to the upper floor, merry farewells at bedroom doors and silence, at last, reigned in the Van Gleck mansion.

Early the next morning the door was solemnly unlocked and opened in the presence of the assembled household; when, lo! a sight appeared, proving St. Nicholas to be a saint of his word.

Every shoe was filled to overflowing; and beside each stood many a colored pile. The table was heavy with its load of presents —candies, toys, trinkets, books, and other articles. Every one had gifts, from grandfather down to the baby.

Little Katy clapped her hands with glee, and vowed inwardly that the cat should never know another moment's grief.

Hendrick capered about the room, flourishing a superb bow and arrows over his head. Hilda laughed with delight as she opened a crimson box, and drew forth its glittering contents. The rest chuckled, and said, "Oh!" and "Ah!" over their treasures, very much as we did here in America on last Christmas Day.

With her glittering necklace in her hands, and a pile of books in her arms, Hilda stole towards her parents, and held up her beaming face for a kiss. There was such an earnest, tender look in her bright eyes, that her mother breathed a blessing as she leaned over her.

"I am delighted with this book: thank you, father!" she said, touching the top one with her chin. "I shall read it all day long."

"Ay, sweetheart," said mynheer, "you cannot do better. There is no one like Father Cats. If my daughter learns his 'Moral Emblem' by heart, the mother and I may keep silent."

(Considering that the back of the book was turned away, mynheer certainly showed a surprising familiarity with an unopened volume presented by St. Nicholas. It was strange, too, that the saint should have found certain things made by the elder children, and had actually placed them upon the table, labeled with parents' and grandparents' names. But all were too much absorbed in happiness to notice slight inconsistencies. Hilda saw on her father's face the rapt expression he always wore when he spoke of Jacob Cats: so she put her armful of books upon the table, and resigned herself to listen.)

"Old Father Cats, my child, was a great poet, not a writer of plays, like the Englishman Shakespeare, who lived in his time. I have read them in the German; and very good they are—very, very good—but not like Father Cats's. He was keeper of the Great Seal of Holland. He was a— Bah! there is too much noise here; I cannot talk." And mynheer, looking with astonishment into the bowl of his meerschaum (for it had gone out) nodded to his vrouw, and left the apartment in great haste.

The fact is, his discourse had been accompanied throughout with a subdued chorus of barking dogs, squeaking cats, and bleating lambs, to say nothing of a noisy ivory cricket, that the baby was whirling with infinite delight. At the last, little Huygens, taking advantage of the increasing loudness of mynheer's tones, had ventured a blast of his new trumpet; and Wolfert had hastily attempted an accompaniment on the drum. This had brought matters to a crisis; and well for the little creatures that it had. The saint had left no ticket for them to attend a lecture on Jacob Cats. It was not an appointed part of the ceremonies. Therefore, when the youngsters saw that the mother looked neither frightened nor offended, they gathered new courage. The grand chorus rose triumphant; and frolic and joy reigned supreme.

Good St. Nicholas! For the sake of the young Hollanders, I, for one, am willing to acknowledge him, and defend his reality against all unbelievers.

2

Uncle Toby's Favorite Christmas Poems—Familiar Lines to Bring Back Pleasant Memories, Together With Some Newcomers Which He Thinks Worthy of Such Genial Company.

"In Excelsis Gloria!"

When Christ was born of Mary free,
In Bethlehem, in that fair citie,
Angels sang there with mirth and glee,
       In Excelsis Gloria!

Herdsmen beheld these angels bright,
To them appearing with great light,
Who said, "God's Son is born this night,"
       In Excelsis Gloria!

This King is come to save mankind,
As in Scripture truths we find,
Therefore this song have we in mind,
       In Excelsis Gloria!

Then, dear Lord, for Thy great grace,
Grant us the bliss to see Thy face,
That we may sing to Thy solace,
       In Excelsis Gloria!

       —Old English Song (circa 1500)

New Christmas

Upon a night of stars a new star rose,
And to lone shepherds on a silent hill
   An Angel spoke.
And these were prelude to a miracle—
   For in His mother's arms a Young Child woke.

Our heavens and earth are clamorous with sound.
Yet this is but a prelude that must pass
   When we shall bend

Before a Babe new born, and know at last
  That of Thy miracles there is no end.

God make us understand, though we are blind,
How empty is the faith that cannot see
  The Christ Child still.
In each new life Thy spirit lives again:
  Thy kingdom for the building, if we will!

—Anne L. New (1935)

Christmas in the Olden Time

(MARMION, *Introduction to Canto VI*)

Heap on more wood!—the wind is chill;
But let it whistle as it will,
We'll keep our Christmas merry still.
Each age has deemed the new-born year
The fittest time for festal cheer:
And well our Christian sires of old
Loved when the year its course had rolled,
And brought blithe Christmas back again,
With all its hospitable train.
Domestic and religious rite
Gave honor to the holy night;
On Christmas eve the bells were rung;
On Christmas eve the mass was sung:
That only night, in all the year,
Saw the stoled priest the chalice rear.
The damsel donned her kirtle sheen;
The hall was dressed with holly green;
Forth to the wood did merry men go,
To gather in the mistletoe.
Then opened wide the baron's hall
To vassal, tenant, serf, and all;
Power laid his rod of rule aside,

And Ceremony doffed his pride.
The heir, with roses in his shoes,
That night might village partner choose.
The lord, underogating, share
The vulgar game of "post and pair."
All hailed, with uncontrolled delight,
And general voice, the happy night,
That to the cottage, as the crown,
Brought tidings of salvation down.
The fire, with well-dried logs supplied,
Went roaring up the chimney wide;
The huge hall-table's oaken face,
Scrubbed till it shone, the day to grace,
Bore then upon its massive board
No mark to part the squire and lord.
Then was brought in the lusty brawn
By old blue-coated serving-man;
Then the grim boar's head frowned on high,
Crested with bays and rosemary.
Well can the green-garbed ranger tell
How, when, and where, the monster fell;
What dogs before his death he tore,
And all the baiting of the boar.
The wassail round, in good brown bowls,
Garnished with ribbons, blithely trowls.
There the huge sirloin reeked; hard by
Plum-porridge stood, and Christmas pie;
Nor failed old Scotland to produce,
At such high tide, her savory goose.
Then came the merry maskers in,
And carols roared with blithesome din;
If unmelodious was the song,
It was a hearty note, and strong.
Who lists may in their mumming see
Traces of ancient mystery;
White shirts supplied the masquerade,
And smutted cheeks the visors made;
But, O! what maskers, richly dight,

Can boast of bosoms half so light!
England was merry England, when
Old Christmas brought his sports again.
'Twas Christmas broached the mightiest ale;
'Twas Christmas told the merriest tale;
A Christmas gambol oft could cheer
The poor man's heart through half the year.

—Sir Walter Scott (1808)

Christmas Lullaby

Sleep, baby, sleep! The Mother sings:
Heaven's angels kneel and fold their wings:
    Sleep, baby, sleep!

With swathes of scented hay thy bed
By Mary's hand at eve was spread.
    Sleep, baby, sleep!

At midnight came the shepherds, they
Whom seraphs wakened by the way.
    Sleep, baby, sleep!

There three kings from the East afar
Ere dawn came guided by Thy star.
    Sleep, baby, sleep!

They brought Thee gifts and gold and gems,
Pure orient pearls, rich diadems.
    Sleep, baby, sleep!

But thou who liest slumbering there
Art King of Kings, earth, ocean, air.
    Sleep, baby, sleep!

Sleep, baby, sleep! The shepherds sing.
Through heaven, through earth, hosannas ring.
Sleep, baby, sleep!

—John Addington Symonds (1885)

Brightest and Best of the Sons of the Morning

Brightest and best of the Sons of the morning,
  Dawn on our darkness, and lend us thine aid!
Star of the East, the horizon adorning,
  Guide where our Infant Redeemer is laid!

Cold on His cradle the dewdrops are shining,
  Low lies His head with the beasts of the stall;
Angels adore Him in slumber reclining,
  Maker and Monarch and Saviour of all.

Shall we not yield Him, in costly devotion,
  Odors of Edom and offerings divine?
Gems of the mountain and pearls of the ocean,
  Myrrh from the forest, or gold from the mine?

Vainly we offer each ampler oblation,
  Vainly with gifts would His favor secure:
Richer by far is the heart's adoration;
  Dearer to God are the prayers of the poor.

Brightest and best of the Sons of the morning,
  Dawn on our darkness, and lend us thine aid!
Star of the East, the horizon adorning,
  Guide where our Infant Redeemer is laid!

—Reginald Heber (1811)

The Vision of Sir Launfal

(Selections from Part Second)

PRELUDE

Down swept the chill wind from the mountain peak,
From the snow five thousand summers old;
On open wold and hilltop bleak
It had gathered all the cold,
And whirled it like sleet on the wanderer's cheek;
It carried a shiver everywhere
From the unleafed boughs and pastures bare;
The little brook heard it and built a roof
'Neath which he could house him, winter-proof;
All night by the white stars' frosty gleams
He groined his arches and matched his beams;
Slender and clear were his crystal spars
As the lashes of light that trim the stars:
He sculptured every summer delight
In his halls and chambers out of sight;
Sometimes his tinkling waters slipt
Down through a frost-leaved forest-crypt,
Long, sparkling aisles of steel-stemmed trees
Bending to counterfeit a breeze;
Sometimes the roof no fretwork knew
But silvery mosses that downward grew;
Sometimes it was carved in sharp relief
With quaint arabesques of ice-fern leaf;
Sometimes it was simply smooth and clear
For the gladness of heaven to shine through, and here
He had caught the nodding bulrush-tops
And hung them thickly with diamond drops,
That crystalled the beams of moon and sun,
And made a star of every one:
No mortal builder's most rare device

Could match this winter-palace of ice;
'T was as if every image that mirrored lay
In his depths serene through the summer day,
Each fleeting shadow of earth and sky,
   Lest the happy model should be lost,
Had been mimicked in fairy masonry
   By the elfin builders of the frost.

Within the hall are song and laughter,
   The cheeks of Christmas glow red and jolly,
And sprouting is every corbel and rafter
   With lightsome green of ivy and holly;
Through the deep gulf of the chimney wide
Wallows the Yule log's roaring tide;
The broad flame-pennons droop and flap
   And belly and tug as a flag in the wind;
Like a locust shrills the imprisoned sap,
   Hunted to death in its galleries blind;
And swift little troops of silent sparks,
   Now pausing, now scattering away as in fear,
Go threading the soot-forest's tangled darks
   Like herds of startled deer.

But the wind without was eager and sharp,
Of Sir Launfal's gray hair it makes a harp,
    And rattles and wrings
    The icy strings,
   Singing, in dreary monotone,
   A Christmas carol of its own,
   Whose burden still, as he might guess,
   Was "Shelterless, shelterless, shelterless!"
The voice of the seneschal flared like a torch
As he shouted the wanderer away from the porch,
And he sat in the gateway and saw all night
   The great hall-fire, so cheery and bold,
   Through the window-slits of the castle old,
Build out its piers of ruddy light
Against the drift of the cold.

I

There was never a leaf on bush or tree,
The bare boughs rattled shudderingly;
The river was dumb and could not speak,
 For the weaver Winter its shroud had spun;
A single crow on the tree-top bleak
 From his shining feathers shed off the cold sun;
Again it was morning, but shrunk and cold,
As if her veins were sapless and old,
And she rose up decrepitly
For a last dim look at earth and sea.

II

Sir Launfal turned from his own hard gate,
For another heir in his earldom sate;
An old, bent man, worn out and frail,
He came back from seeking the Holy Grail;
Little he recked of his earldom's loss,
No more on his surcoat was blazoned the cross,
But deep in his soul the sign he wore,
The badge of the suffering and the poor.

III

Sir Launfal's raiment thin and spare
Was idle mail 'gainst the barbèd air,
For it was just at the Christmas time;
So he mused, as he sat, of a sunnier clime,
And sought for a shelter from cold and snow
In the light and warmth of long-ago;
He sees the snake-like caravan crawl
O'er the edge of the desert, black and small,
Then nearer and nearer, till, one by one,
He can count the camels in the sun,
As over the red-hot sands they pass

To where, in its slender necklace of grass,
The little spring laughed and leapt in the shade,
And with its own self like an infant played,
And waved its signal of palms.

IV

"For Christ's sweet sake, I beg an alms;"
The happy camels may reach the spring,
But Sir Launfal sees only the grewsome thing,
The leper, lank as the rain-blanched bone,
That cowers beside him, a thing as lone
And white as the ice-isles of Northern seas
In the desolate horror of his disease.

V

And Sir Launfal said, "I behold in thee
An image of Him who died on the tree;
Thou also hast had thy crown of thorns,
Thou also hast had the world's buffets and scorns,
And to thy life were not denied
The wounds in the hands and feet and side:
Mild Mary's Son, acknowledge me;
Behold, through Him, I give to thee!"

VI

Then the soul of the leper stood up in his eyes
    And looked at Sir Launfal, and straightway he
Remembered in what a haughtier guise
    He had flung an alms to leprosie,
When he girt his young life up in gilded mail
And set forth in search of the Holy Grail.
The heart within him was ashes and dust;
He parted in twain his single crust,
He broke the ice on the streamlet's brink,
And gave the leper to eat and drink,

'T was a mouldy crust of coarse brown bread,
  'T was water out of a wooden bowl,—
Yet with fine wheaten bread was the leper fed,
  And 't was red wine he drank with his thirsty soul.

VII

As Sir Launfal mused with a downcast face,
A light shone round about the place;
The leper no longer crouched at his side,
But stood before him glorified,
Shining and tall and fair and straight
As the pillar that stood by the Beautiful Gate,—
Himself the Gate whereby men can
Enter the temple of God in Man.

VIII

His words were shed softer than leaves from the pine,
And they fell on Sir Launfal as snows on the brine,
That mingle their softness and quiet in one
With the shaggy unrest they float down upon;
And the voice that was softer than silence said,
"Lo, it is I, be not afraid!
In many climes, without avail,
Thou hast spent thy life for the Holy Grail;
Behold, it is here,—this cup which thou
Didst fill at the streamlet for me but now;
This crust is my body broken for thee,
This water his blood that died on the tree;
The Holy Supper is kept, indeed,
In whatso we share with another's need;
Not what we give, but what we share,
For the gift without the giver is bare;
Who gives himself with his alms feeds three,
Himself, his hungering neighbor, and me."

—James Russell Lowell (1848)

Awake, Glad Heart!

Awake, glad heart! Get up, and sing!
It is the birthday of thy King.
    Awake! Awake!
    The sun doth shake
Light from his locks, and all the way
Breathing perfumes, doth spice the day.

I would I were some bird, or star,
Fluttering in woods, or lifted far
    Above this inn
    And road of sin!
Then either star, or bird, should be
Shining, or singing, still to Thee.

—*Henry Vaughan (1650)*

A Christmas Carol

In the bleak mid-winter
    Frosty wind made moan,
Earth stood hard as iron,
    Water like a stone;
Snow had fallen, snow on snow,
    Snow on snow,
In the bleak mid-winter
    Long ago.

Our God, Heaven cannot hold Him,
    Nor earth sustain;

Heaven and earth shall flee away
  When He comes to reign:
In the bleak mid-winter
  A stable-place sufficed
The Lord God Almighty,
  Jesus Christ.

Enough for Him, whom cherubim
  Worship night and day,
A breastful of milk
  And a mangerful of hay;
Enough for Him whom angels
  Fall down before,
The ox and ass and camel
  Which adore.

Angels and archangels
  May have gathered there,
Cherubim and seraphim
  Throng'd the air;
But only His mother
  In her maiden bliss
Worshipped the Beloved
  With a kiss.

What can I give Him,
  Poor as I am?
If I were a shepherd
  I would bring a lamb,
If I were a Wise Man
  I would do my part,—
Yet what I can I give Him,
  Give my heart.

—*Christina Georgina Rossetti (1871)*

Away in a Manger

Away in a manger,
  No crib for His bed,
The little Lord Jesus
  Laid down His sweet head.

The stars in the bright sky
  Look'd down where He lay,
The little Lord Jesus
  Asleep in the hay.

The cattle are lowing,
  The poor Baby wakes,
But little Lord Jesus,
  No crying He makes.

I love Thee, Lord Jesus;
  Look down from the sky,
And stay by my crib,
  Watching my lullaby.

        —*Martin Luther (circa 1500)*

3

Six Yuletide Short Stories Uncle Toby Has
Chosen With Special Care—Smiles Here, Tears
There, but the Christmas Spirit Everywhere.
He Likes to Read the First One Out Loud.

A Christmas Carol

In Prose, Being a Ghost Story of Christmas
(which can be read in 42 minutes)

By CHARLES DICKENS

Stave One: MARLEY'S GHOST

MARLEY was dead, to begin with. There is no doubt whatever about that. The register of his burial was signed by the clergyman, the clerk, the undertaker, and the chief mourner. Scrooge signed it. And Scrooge's name was good upon 'Change, for anything he chose to put his hand to.

Old Marley was as dead as a door-nail.

Scrooge and he had been partners for many, many years.

Scrooge was his sole executor, his sole administrator, his sole assign, his sole residuary legatee, his sole friend, and sole mourner. And even Scrooge was not so dreadfully cut up by the sad event but that he was an excellent man of business on the very day of the funeral, and solemnized it with an undoubted bargain.

Scrooge never painted out Old Marley's name. There it stood, years afterward, above the warehouse door: Scrooge & Marley. The firm was known as Scrooge & Marley. Sometimes people new to the business called Scrooge Scrooge, and sometimes Marley, but he answered to both names. It was all the same to him.

Oh! But he was a tight-fisted hand at the grindstone, Scrooge! a squeezing, wrenching, grasping, scraping, clutching, covetous, old sinner! Hard and sharp as flint, from which no steel had ever struck out generous fire; secret, and self-contained, and solitary as an oyster. The cold within him froze his old features, nipped his pointed nose, shrivelled his cheek, stiffened his gait; made his eyes red, his thin lips blue; and spoke out shrewdly in his grating voice. A frosty rime was on his head, and on his eyebrows, and his wiry chin. He carried his own low temperature always about with him; he iced his office in the dog-days; and didn't thaw it one degree at Christmas.

Nobody ever stopped him in the street to say, with gladsome looks, "My dear Scrooge, how are you? When will you come to see me?" No beggars implored him to bestow a trifle, no children asked him what it was o'clock, no man or woman ever once in all his life inquired the way to such and such a place, of Scrooge.

But what did Scrooge care! It was the very thing he liked. To edge his way along the crowded paths of life, warning all human sympathy to keep its distance, was what the knowing ones call "nuts" to Scrooge.

Once upon a time—of all the good days in the year, on Christmas Eve—old Scrooge sat busy in his counting-house. It was cold, bleak, biting weather; foggy withal.

The door of Scrooge's counting-house was open that he might keep his eye upon his clerk, who in a dismal little cell beyond, a sort of tank, was copying letters. Scrooge had a very small fire, but the clerk's fire was so very much smaller that it looked like one coal. But he couldn't replenish it, for Scrooge kept the coal-box in his own room; and so surely as the clerk came in with the shovel, the master predicted that it would be necessary for them to part. Wherefore the clerk put on his white comforter, and tried to warm himself at the candle; in which effort, not being a man of a strong imagination, he failed.

"A merry Christmas, uncle! God save you!" cried a cheerful voice. It was the voice of Scrooge's nephew, who came upon him so quickly that this was the first intimation he had of his approach.

"Bah!" said Scrooge. "Humbug!"

"Christmas a humbug, uncle!" said Scrooge's nephew. "You don't mean that, I am sure?"

"I do," said Scrooge. "Merry Christmas! What right have you to be merry? You're poor enough."

"Come, then," returned the nephew gayly. "What right have you to be dismal? You're rich enough."

Scrooge, having no better answer ready on the spur of the moment, said "Bah!" again; and followed it up with "Humbug."

"Don't be cross, uncle!" said the nephew.

"What else can I be," returned the uncle, "when I live in such a world of fools as this? What's Christmas time to you but a time for paying bills without money; a time for finding yourself a year older, and not an hour richer. If I could work my will," said

Scrooge indignantly, "every idiot who goes about with 'Merry Christmas' on his lips, should be boiled with his own pudding, and buried with a stake of holly through his heart. He should!"

"Don't be angry, uncle. Come! Dine with us tomorrow."

Scrooge said that he would see him—yes, indeed he did. He went the whole length of the expression, and said that he would see him in that extremity first.

"But why?" cried Scrooge's nephew. "Why?"

"Good afternoon," said Scrooge.

"I am sorry, with all my heart, to find you so resolute. We have never had any quarrel, to which I have been a party. But I have made the trial in homage to Christmas, and I'll keep my Christmas humour to the last. So a merry Christmas, uncle!"

"Good afternoon!" said Scrooge.

"And A Happy New Year!"

"Good afternoon!" said Scrooge.

His nephew stopped at the outer door to bestow the greetings of the season on the clerk, who, cold as he was, was warmer than Scrooge; for he returned them cordially.

"There's another fellow," muttered Scrooge; who overheard him; "my clerk, with fifteen shillings a week, and a wife and family, talking about a merry Christmas. I'll retire to Bedlam."

The clerk, in letting Scrooge's nephew out, had let two other people in. They were portly gentlemen, pleasant to behold, and now stood, with their hats off, in Scrooge's office.

"At this festive season of the year, Mr. Scrooge," said one of the gentlemen, "it is more than usually desirable that we should make some slight provision for the poor and destitute, who suffer greatly at the present time. Many thousands are in want of common necessaries; hundreds of thousands are in want of common comforts, sir."

"Are there no prisons?" asked Scrooge.

"Plenty of prisons," said the gentleman.

"And the Union workhouses?" demanded Scrooge. "Are they still in operation?"

"They are," returned the gentleman. "Under the impression that they scarcely furnish Christmas cheer of mind or body to the multitude, a few of us are endeavouring to raise a fund to buy the poor some meat and drink, and means of warmth. We choose this time, because it is a time, of all others, when Want is keenly felt, and Abundance rejoices. What shall I put you down for?"

"Nothing!" Scrooge replied.

"You wish to be anonymous?"

"I wish to be left alone," said Scrooge. "I help to support the establishments I have mentioned—they cost enough; and those who are badly off must go there."

"Many can't go there; and many would rather die."

"If they would rather die," said Scrooge, "they had better do it, and decrease the surplus population. Good afternoon, gentlemen!"

Seeing clearly that it would be useless to pursue their point, the gentlemen withdrew. Scrooge resumed his labours with an improved opinion of himself, and in a more facetious temper than was usual with him.

At length the hour of shutting up the counting-house arrived. With an ill will Scrooge dismounted from his stool, and tacitly admitted the fact to the expectant clerk in the tank, who instantly snuffed his candle out, and put on his hat.

"You'll want all day tomorrow, I suppose?" said Scrooge.

"If quite convenient, sir."

"It's not convenient," said Scrooge, "and it's not fair. If I was to stop half-a-crown for it, you'd think yourself ill-used, I'll be bound?"

The clerk smiled faintly.

"And yet," said Scrooge, "you don't think *me* ill-used when I pay a day's wages for no work."

The clerk observed that it was only once a year.

"A poor excuse for picking a man's pocket every twenty-fifth of December!" said Scrooge, buttoning his great-coat to the chin. "But I suppose you must have the whole day. Be here the earlier next morning."

The clerk promised that he would; and Scrooge walked out with a growl.

Scrooge took his melancholy dinner in his usual melancholy tavern; and having read all the newspapers, and beguiled the rest of the evening with his banker's book, went home to bed. He lived in chambers which had once belonged to his deceased partner. They were a gloomy suite of rooms, in a lowering pile of building up a yard. Nobody lived in it but Scrooge, the other rooms being all let out as offices. The yard was so dark that even Scrooge, who knew its every stone, was fain to grope with his hands.

Now, it is a fact that there was nothing at all particular about the knocker on the door, except that it was very large. Let it also be borne in mind that Scrooge had not been thinking of Marley. And then let any man explain to me, if he can, how it happened that Scrooge, having his key in the lock of the door, saw in the knocker, without its undergoing any intermediate process of change—not a knocker, but Marley's face.

Marley's face. It was not in impenetrable shadow as the other objects in the yard were, but had a dismal light about it, like a bad lobster in a dark cellar. It was not angry or ferocious, but looked at Scrooge as Marley used to look; with ghostly spectacles turned up on its ghostly forehead.

As Scrooge looked fixedly at this phenomenon, it was a knocker again.

To say that he was not startled, or that his blood was not conscious of a terrible sensation to which it had been a stranger from infancy, would be untrue. But he put his hand upon the key he had relinquished, turned it sturdily, walked in, and lighted his candle.

He *did* pause, with a moment's irresolution, before he shut the door; and he *did* look cautiously behind at first, as if he half-expected to be terrified with the sight of Marley's pigtail sticking out into the hall. But there was nothing on the back of the door except the screws and nuts that held the knocker on.

Quite satisfied, he locked himself in; double-locked himself in, which was not his custom. Thus secured against surprise, he took off his cravat, put on his dressing-gown and slippers and his night-cap; and sat down before the fire to take his gruel.

The fireplace was an old one, built by some Dutch merchant long ago, and paved all around with quaint Dutch tiles, designed to illustrate the Scriptures. There were Cains and Abels, Pharaoh's daughters, Queens of Sheba, Angelic messengers descending through the air on clouds like featherbeds, Abrahams, Belshazzars, Apostles putting off to sea in butter-boats, hundreds of figures to attract his thoughts; and yet that face of Marley, seven years dead, came like the ancient Prophet's rod, and swallowed up the whole. If each smooth tile had been a blank at first, with power to shape some picture on its surface from the disjointed fragments of his thoughts, there would have been a copy of old Marley's head on every one.

"Humbug!" said Scrooge; and walked across the room.

After several turns, he sat down again. As he threw his head back in the chair, his glance happened to rest upon a bell, a disused

bell, that hung in the room. It was with great astonishment, and with a strange, inexplicable dread that, as he looked he saw this bell begin to swing. It swung so softly in the outset that it scarcely made a sound; but soon it rang out loudly, and so did every bell in the house.

This might have lasted half a minute, or a minute, but it seemed an hour. The bells ceased as they had begun, together. They were succeeded by a clanking noise, deep down below; as if some person were dragging a heavy chain over the casks in the wine merchant's cellar.

The cellar door flew open with a booming sound, and then he heard the noise coming up the stairs; then coming straight towards his door.

"It's humbug still!" said Scrooge. "I won't believe it."

His colour changed, though, when, without a pause, it came on through the heavy door, and passed into the room before his eyes. Upon its coming in, the dying flame leaped up, as though it cried "I know him; Marley's Ghost!" and fell again.

The same face; the very same. Marley in his pigtail, usual waistcoat, tights and boots. The chain he drew was clasped about his middle. It was long, and wound about him like a tail; and it was made (for Scrooge observed it closely) of cash-boxes, keys, padlocks, ledgers, deeds, and heavy purses wrought in steel. His body was transparent; so that Scrooge, observing him and looking through his waistcoat, could see the two buttons on his coat behind.

Scrooge had often heard it said that Marley had no bowels, but he had never believed it until now.

Though he looked the phantom through and through, and marked the very texture of the folded kerchief bound about its head and chin, which wrapper he had not observed before, he was still incredulous, and fought against his senses.

"How now!" said Scrooge, caustic and cold as ever. "What do you want with me?"

"Much!"—Marley's voice, no doubt about it.

"Who are you?"

"In life I was your partner, Jacob Marley."

The Ghost sat down on the opposite side of the fireplace, as if he were quite used to it.

"You don't believe in me," he observed.

"I don't," said Scrooge.

"What evidence would you have of my reality beyond that of your senses?"

"I don't know," said Scrooge.

"Why do you doubt your senses?"

"Because," said Scrooge, "a little thing affects them. A slight disorder of the stomach makes them cheats. You may be an undigested bit of beef, a blot of mustard, a crumb of cheese, a fragment of an underdone potato. There's more of gravy than of grave about you, whatever you are!"

Scrooge was not much in the habit of cracking jokes, nor did he feel, in his heart, by any means waggish then. The truth is that he tried to be smart, as a means of distracting his own attention, and keeping down his terror; for the spectre's voice disturbed the very marrow in his bones.

"You see this toothpick?" said Scrooge, returning quickly to the charge.

"I do," replied the Ghost.

"Well!" returned Scrooge, "I have but to swallow this, and be for the rest of my days persecuted by a legion of goblins, all of my own creation. Humbug, I tell you! humbug!"

At this the spirit raised a frightful cry, and shook its chain with such a dismal and appalling noise that Scrooge held on tight to his chair, to save himself from falling in a swoon. But how much greater was his terror when the phantom, taking off the bandage round its head, as if it were too warm to wear indoors, its lower jaw dropped down upon its breast!

Scrooge fell upon his knees, and clasped his hands before his face.

"Man of the worldly mind!" said the Ghost, "do you believe in me or not?"

"I do," said Scrooge. "I must. But why do spirits walk the earth, and why do they come to me?"

"It is required of every man," the Ghost returned, "that the spirit within him should walk abroad among his fellow-men, and travel far and wide; and if that spirit goes not forth in life, it is condemned to do so after death. It is doomed to wander through the world—oh, woe is me!—and witness what it cannot share, but might have shared on earth, and turned to happiness!"

Again the spectre raised a cry, and shook its chain and wrung its shadowy hands.

"You are fettered," said Scrooge, trembling. "Tell me why?"

"I wear the chain I forged in life," replied the Ghost. "I made it link by link and yard by yard; I girded it on of my own free will. Is its pattern strange to *you*?"

Scrooge trembled more and more.

"Or would you know," pursued the Ghost, "the weight and length of the strong coil you bear yourself? It is a ponderous chain!"

Scrooge glanced about him on the floor, in the expectation of finding himself surrounded by some fifty or sixty fathoms of iron cable; but he could see nothing.

"Jacob," he said, imploringly. "Old Jacob Marley, tell me more. Speak comfort to me, Jacob!"

"I have none to give," the Ghost replied. "It comes from other regions, Ebenezer Scrooge, and is conveyed by other ministers, to other kinds of men. I cannot rest, I cannot linger anywhere. My spirit never walked beyond our counting-house—mark me!—in life my spirit never roved beyond the narrow limits of our money-changing hole; and weary journeys lie before me!"

"You must have been very slow about it, Jacob," Scrooge observed, in a business-like manner, though with humility and deference.

"Slow!" the Ghost repeated.

"Seven years dead," mused Scrooge. "And traveling all the time?"

"The whole time," said the Ghost. "No rest, no peace. Incessant torture of remorse."

"You travel fast?" said Scrooge.

"On the wings of the wind," replied the Ghost.

"You might have got over a great quantity of ground in seven years," said Scrooge.

The Ghost, on hearing this, set up another cry, and clanked its chain hideously.

"Oh! captive, bound and double-ironed," cried the phantom, "not to know that any Christian spirit working kindly in its little sphere, whatever it may be, will find its mortal life too short for its vast means of usefulness. Not to know that no space of regret can make amends for one life's opportunity misused! Yet such was I! Oh! such was I!"

"But you were always a good man of business, Jacob," faltered Scrooge, who now began to apply this to himself.

"Business!" cried the Ghost, wringing its hands again. "Mankind was my business. The common welfare was my business; charity, mercy, forbearance, and benevolence were, all, my business. The dealings of my trade were but a drop of water in the comprehensive ocean of my business!"

Scrooge was very much dismayed to hear the spectre going on at this rate, and began to quake exceedingly.

"Hear me!" cried the Ghost. "My time is nearly gone."

"I will," said Scrooge. "But don't be hard upon me! Don't be flowery, Jacob! Pray!"

"How it is that I appear before you in a shape that you can see, I may not tell. I have sat invisible beside you many and many a day."

It was not an agreeable idea. Scrooge shivered, and wiped the perspiration from his brow.

"That is no light part of my penance," pursued the Ghost. "I am here tonight to warn you that you have yet a chance and hope of escaping my fate. A chance and hope of my procuring, Ebenezer."

"You were always a good friend to me," said Scrooge. "Thank'ee!"

"You will be haunted," resumed the Ghost, "by Three Spirits."

Scrooge's countenance fell almost as low as the Ghost's had done.

"I—I think I'd rather not," said Scrooge.

"Without their visits," said the Ghost, "you cannot hope to shun the path I tread. Expect the first tomorrow, when the bell tolls One."

"Couldn't I take 'em all at once, and have it over, Jacob?" hinted Scrooge.

"Expect the second on the next night at the same hour. The third upon the next night when the last stroke of Twelve has ceased to vibrate. Look to see me no more; and look that, for your own sake, you remember what has passed between us!"

When it had said these words, the spectre took its wrapper from the table, and bound it round its head, as before. Scrooge knew this, by the smart sound its teeth made, when the jaws were brought together by the bandage. He ventured to raise his eyes again, and found his supernatural visitor confronting him, with its chain wound over and about its arm.

The apparition walked backward from him; and at every step it took, the window raised itself a little, so that when the spectre reached it it was wide open.

Scrooge became sensible of confused noises in the air; incoherent sounds of lamentation and regret; wailings inexpressibly sorrowful and self-accusatory. The spectre, after listening for a moment, joined in the mournful dirge, and floated out upon the bleak, dark night.

Scrooge followed to the window, desperate in his curiosity. He looked out.

The air was filled with Phantoms, wandering hither and thither in restless haste, and moaning as they went. Every one of them wore chains like Marley's Ghost; some few (they might be guilty governments) were linked together; none were free. Many had been personally known to Scrooge in their lives.

Whether these creatures faded into mist, or mist enshrouded them, he could not tell. But they and their spirit voices faded together; and the night became as it had been when he walked home.

Scrooge closed the window, and examined the door by which the Ghost has entered. The bolts were undisturbed. He tried to say "Humbug!" but stopped at the first syllable. And being from the emotion he had undergone much in need of repose, went straight to bed, without undressing, and fell asleep upon the instant.

Stave Two: THE FIRST OF THE THREE SPIRITS

When Scrooge awoke it was so dark that, looking out of bed, he could scarcely distinguish the transparent window from the opaque walls of his chamber. He was endeavoring to pierce the darkness with his ferret eyes, when the chimes of a neighbouring church struck the four quarters. So he listened for the hour.

Twelve! It was past two when he went to bed. The clock was wrong. An icicle must have got into the works. Twelve!

He resolved to lie awake until the hour was passed; and, considering that he could no more go to sleep than go to Heaven, this was perhaps the wisest resolution in his power.

The hour was so long that he was more than once convinced he must have sunk into a doze unconsciously, and missed the clock. At length it broke upon his listening ear.

One. Light flashed up in the room upon the instant, and the curtains of his bed were drawn.

The curtains of his bed were drawn aside, I tell you, by a hand, and Scrooge starting up into a half-recumbent attitude, found himself face to face with the unearthly visitor who drew them: as close to it as I am now to you, and I am standing in the spirit at your elbow.

It was a strange figure—like a child; yet not so like a child as like an old man, viewed through some supernatural medium which gave it the appearance of having receded from the view, and being diminished to a child's proportions. Its hair, which hung about its neck and down its back, was white as if with age; and yet the face had not a wrinkle in it, and the tenderest bloom was on the skin. It wore a tunic of the purest white; and round its waist was bound a lustrous belt, the sheen of which was beautiful. It held a branch of fresh green holly in its hand; and, in singular contradiction of that wintry emblem, had its dress trimmed with summer flowers. But the strangest thing about it was that from the crown of its head there sprang a bright clear jet of light, by which all this was visible; and which was doubtless the occasion of its using, in its duller moments, a great extinguisher for a cap, which it now held under its arm.

"Are you the Spirit, sir, whose coming was foretold to me?" asked Scrooge.

"I am!"

The voice was soft and gentle. Singularly low, as if instead of being so close beside him, it were at a distance.

"Who, and what are you?" Scrooge demanded.

"I am the Ghost of Christmas Past."

"Long Past?" inquired Scrooge, observant of its dwarfish stature.

"No. Your past."

Perhaps Scrooge could not have told anybody why, if anybody could have asked him; but he had a special desire to see the Spirit in his cap; and begged him to be covered.

"What!" exclaimed the Ghost, "would you so soon put out, with worldly hands, the light I give? Is it not enough that you are one of those whose passions made this cap, and force me through whole trains of years to wear it low upon my brow!"

Scrooge reverently disclaimed all intention to offend or any knowledge of having wilfully "bonneted" the Spirit at any period of his life. He then made bold to inquire what business brought him there.

"Your welfare!" said the Ghost.

Scrooge expressed himself much obliged, but could not help thinking that a night of unbroken rest would have been more conducive to that end. The Spirit must have heard him thinking, for it said immediately:

"Your reclamation, then. Take heed!"

It put out its strong hand as it spoke, and clasped him gently by the arm.

"Rise! and walk with me!"

As the words were spoken, they passed through the wall, and stood upon an open country road, with fields on either hand. The city had entirely vanished. The darkness and the mist had vanished with it, for it was a clear, cold winter day, with snow upon the ground.

"Good Heaven!" said Scrooge, clasping his hands together as he looked about him. "I was bred in this place. I was a boy here!"

"You recollect the way?" inquired the Spirit.

"Remember it!" cried Scrooge with fervor. "I could walk it blindfold."

They left the highroad, and soon approached the school of dull red brick. It was a large house, but one of broken fortunes; for the spacious offices were little used, their walls were damp and mossy, their windows broken, and their gates decayed.

They went, the Ghost and Scrooge, to a door at the back of the house. It opened before them, and disclosed a long, bare, melancholy room, made barer still by lines of plain deal forms and desks. At one of these a lonely boy was reading near a feeble fire; and Scrooge sat down upon a form, and wept to see his poor forgotten self as he used to be.

The Ghost smiled thoughtfully, and waved its hand; saying as it did so, "Let us see a merry Christmas!"

Scrooge's former self grew larger at the words, and the room became a little darker and more dirty. There he was, alone again, when all the other boys had gone home for the jolly holidays.

He was not reading now, but walking up and down despairingly. Scrooge looked at the Ghost, and with a mournful shaking of his head, glanced anxiously towards the door.

It opened; and a little girl, much younger than the boy, came darting in, and putting her arms about his neck, and often kissing him, addressed him as her "Dear, dear brother."

"I have come to bring you home, dear brother!" said the child, clapping her tiny hands, and bending down to laugh.

"Home, little Fan?" returned the boy.

"Yes!" said the child, brimful of glee. "Home for good and all. Home for ever and ever. Father is so much kinder than he used to be that home's like Heaven! He spoke so gently to me one dear night when I was going to bed that I was not afraid to ask him once more if you might come home; and he said Yes, you should; and sent me in a coach to bring you. And you're to be a man!" said the child, opening her eyes, "and are never to come back here; but first, we're to be together all the Christmas long, and have the merriest time in all the world."

"You are quite a woman, little Fan!" exclaimed the boy.

She clapped her hands and laughed, and tried to touch his head; but being too little, laughed again, and stood on tiptoe to embrace him. Then she began to drag him, in her childish eagerness, towards the door; and he, nothing loath to go, accompanied her.

"Always a delicate creature, whom a breath might have withered," said the Ghost. "But she had a large heart!"

"So she had," cried Scrooge.

"She died a woman," said the Ghost, "and had, as I think, children."

"One child," Scrooge returned.

"True," said the Ghost. "Your nephew!"

Scrooge seemed uneasy in his mind; and answered briefly, "Yes."

Although they had but that moment left the school behind them, they were now in the busy thoroughfares of a city. It was made plain enough, by the dressing of the shops, that here too it was Christmas time again; but it was evening, and the streets were lighted up.

The Ghost stopped at a certain warehouse door, and asked Scrooge if he knew it.

"Know it!" said Scrooge. "Was I apprenticed here!"

They went in. At sight of an old gentleman in a Welsh wig, sitting behind such a high desk that if he had been two inches taller he must have knocked his head against the ceiling, Scrooge cried in great excitement:

"Why, it's old Fezziwig! Bless his heart; it's Fezziwig alive again!"

Old Fezziwig laid down his pen and looked up at the clock, which pointed to the hour of seven. He rubbed his hands; adjusted his capacious waistcoat; laughed all over himself, from his shoes to his organ of benevolence; and called out in a comfortable, oily, rich, fat, jovial voice:

"Yo ho, there! Ebenezer! Dick!"

Scrooge's former self, now grown a young man, came briskly in, accompanied by his fellow-'prentice, Dick Wilkins.

"Hilli-ho, my boys!" said Fezziwig. "No more work tonight. Christmas Eve, Dick. Christmas, Ebenezer! Clear away, my lads, and let's have lots of room here! Hilli-ho, Dick! Chirrup, Ebenezer!"

Clear away! There was nothing they wouldn't have cleared away, or couldn't have cleared away, with old Fezziwig looking on. It was done in a minute. Every movable was packed off, as if it were dismissed from public life for evermore; and the warehouse was as snug, and warm, and dry, and bright a ballroom, as you would desire to see upon a winter's night.

In came a fiddler with a music-book, and went up to the lofty desk, and made an orchestra of it, and tuned like fifty stomach-aches. In came Mrs. Fezziwig, one vast substantial smile. In came the three Miss Fezziwigs, beaming and lovable. In came the six young followers whose hearts they broke. In came all the young men and women employed in the business. In came the housemaid, with her cousin, the baker. In came the cook, with her brother's particular friend, the milkman. In came the boy from over the way, who was suspected of not having board enough from his master; trying to hide himself behind the girl next door but one, who was proved to have had her ears pulled by her mistress. In they all came, one after another. Away they all went, twenty couple at once; hands half round and back again the other way; down the middle and up again.

There were more dances, and there were forfeits, and more dances, and there was cake, and there was negus, and there was a great piece of Cold Roast, and there was a great piece of Cold Boiled, and there were mince pies, and plenty of beer. But the great effect of the evening came after the Roast and Boiled, when

the fiddler struck up "Sir Roger de Coverley." Then old Fezziwig
stood out to dance with Mrs. Fezziwig. As to *her*, she was worthy
to be his partner in every sense of the term. If that's not high
praise, tell me higher, and I'll use it. A positive light appeared to
issue from Fezziwig's calves. They shone in every part of the
dance like moons.

When the clock struck eleven, this domestic ball broke up. Mr.
and Mrs. Fezziwig took their stations, one on either side of the
door, and, shaking hands with every person individually as he or
she went out, wished him or her a merry Christmas.

During the whole of this time, Scrooge had acted like a man out
of his wits. His heart and soul were in the scene, and with his
former self. He corroborated everything, remembered everything,
enjoyed everything, and underwent the strangest agitation. It was
not until now, when the bright faces of his former self and Dick
were turned from them, that he remembered the Ghost, and became conscious that it was looking full upon him, while the light
upon its head burnt very clear.

"A small matter," said the Ghost, "to make these silly folks so
full of gratitude."

"Small!" echoed Scrooge.

"Why! Is it not? He has spent but a few pounds of your mortal
money; three or four perhaps. Is that so much that he deserves
this praise?"

"It isn't that," said Scrooge, heated by the remark, and speaking unconsciously like his former, not his latter, self. "It isn't that,
Spirit. The happiness he gives is quite as great as if it cost a
fortune."

He felt the Spirit's glance, and stopped.

"What is the matter?" asked the Ghost.

"Nothing particular," said Scrooge. "I should like to be able
to say a word or two to my clerk just now. That's all."

His former self turned down the lamps as he gave utterance to
the wish; and Scrooge and the Ghost again stood side by side in
the open air.

Again Scrooge saw himself. He was older now; a man in the
prime of life. His face had not the harsh and rigid lines of later
years; but it had begun to wear the signs of care and avarice.

He was not alone, but sat by the side of a fair young girl in a mourning-dress; in whose eyes there were tears.

"It matters little," she said, softly. "To you, very little. Another idol has displaced me; and if it can cheer and comfort you in time to come, as I would have tried to do, I have no just cause to grieve."

"What idol has displaced you?" he rejoined.

"A golden one."

"This is the even-handed dealing of the world!" he said. "There is nothing on which it is so hard as poverty; and there is nothing it professes to condemn with such severity as the pursuit of wealth!"

"You fear the world too much," she answered, gently. "All your other hopes have merged into the hope of being beyond the chance of its sordid reproach. I have seen your nobler aspirations fall off one by one, until the master-passion, Gain, engrosses you. Have I not?"

"What then?" he retorted. "Even if I have grown so much wiser, what then? I am not changed towards you."

She shook her head.

"Am I?"

"Our contract is an old one. It was made when we were both poor. You *are* changed. When it was made, you were another man."

"I was a boy," he said impatiently.

"Your own feeling tells you that you were not what you are," she returned. "I am. How often and how keenly I have thought of this, I will not say. It is enough that I *have* thought of it, and can release you."

"Have I ever sought release?"

"In words. No. Never."

"In what, then?"

"In a changed nature; in an altered spirit. In everything that made my love of any worth or value in your sight. I release you. With a full heart, for the love of him you once were. May you be happy in the life you have chosen!"

She left him and they parted.

"Spirit!" said Scrooge. "Show me no more! Why do you delight to torture me?"

"One shadow more!" exclaimed the Ghost.

They were in another scene and place; a room, not very large or handsome, but full of comfort. Near to the winter fire sat a beautiful young girl, so like that last that Scrooge believed it was the same, until he saw *her*, now a comely matron, sitting opposite her daughter. The noise in this room was perfectly tumultuous, for there were more children there than Scrooge in his agitated state of mind could count; and, unlike the celebrated herd in the poem, there were not forty children conducting themselves like one, but every child was conducting itself like forty.

But now a knocking at the door was heard and the father came home attended by a man laden with Christmas toys and presents. Then the shouting and the struggling, and the onslaught that was made on the defenceless porter! The joy, and gratitude, and ecstasy! They are all indescribable alike. It is enough that by degrees the children and their emotions got out of the parlor and by one stair at a time, up to the top of the house; where they went to bed, and so subsided.

And now Scrooge looked on more attentively than ever, when the master of the house, having his daughter leaning fondly on him, sat down with her and her mother at his own fireside.

"Belle," said the husband, turning to his wife with a smile, "I saw an old friend of yours this afternoon."

"Who was it?"

"Guess!"

"How can I? Tut, don't I know," she added in the same breath, laughing as he laughed. "Mr. Scrooge."

"Mr. Scrooge it was. I passed his office window; and as it was not shut up, and he had a candle inside, I could scarcely help seeing him. His partner lies upon the point of death, I hear; and there he sat alone. Quite alone in the world, I do believe."

"Spirit!" said Scrooge in a broken voice, "remove me from this place. I cannot bear it!"

He turned upon the Ghost, and seeing that it looked upon him with a face in which in some strange way there were fragments of all the faces it had shown him, wrestled with it.

In the struggle, Scrooge seized the extinguisher-cap, and by a sudden action pressed it down upon its head.

The Spirit dropped beneath it, so that the extinguisher covered its whole form; but though Scrooge pressed it down with all his force, he could not hide the light, which streamed from under it, in an unbroken flood upon the ground.

He was conscious of being exhausted, and overcome by an irresistible drowsiness; and, further, of being in his own bedroom. He gave the cap a parting squeeze, in which his hand relaxed; and had barely time to reel to bed before he sank into a heavy sleep.

Stave Three: THE SECOND OF THE THREE SPIRITS

Awaking in the middle of a prodigiously tough snore, and sitting up in bed to get his thoughts together, Scrooge had no occasion to be told that the bell was again upon the stroke of One. He got up softly and shuffled in his slippers to the door.

The moment Scrooge's hand was on the lock, a strange voice called him by his name and bade him enter. He obeyed.

It was his own room. There was no doubt about that. But it had undergone a surprising transformation. The walls and ceiling were so hung with living green that it looked a perfect grove; from every part of which bright gleaming berries glistened. And such a mighty blaze went roaring up the chimney, as that dull petrifaction of a hearth had never known in Scrooge's time, or Marley's, or for many and many a winter season gone. Heaped upon the floor, to form a kind of throne, were turkeys, geese, game, poultry, brawn, great joints of meat, sucking-pigs, long wreaths of sausages, mince-pies, plum-puddings, barrels of oysters, red-hot chestnuts, cherry-cheeked apples, juicy oranges, luscious pears, immense twelfth-cakes, and seething bowls of punch, that made the chamber dim with their delicious steam. In easy state upon this couch there sat a jolly Giant, glorious to see; who bore a glowing torch, in shape not unlike Plenty's horn, and held it up, high up, to shed its light on Scrooge, as he came peeping round the door.

"Come in!" exclaimed the Ghost. "Come in! and know me better, man!"

Scrooge entered timidly, and hung his head before this Spirit. "I am the Ghost of Christmas Present," said the Spirit. "Look upon me!"

Scrooge reverently did so. It was clothed in one simple green robe, or mantle, bordered with white fur. Its feet, observable beneath the ample folds of the garment, were bare; and on its head it wore no other covering than a holly wreath, set here and there with shining icicles.

The Ghost of Christmas Present rose.

"Spirit," said Scrooge submissively, "conduct me where you will. If you have aught to teach me, let me profit by it."

"Touch my robe!"

Scrooge did as he was told, and held it fast.

Holly, mistletoe, red berries, ivy, turkeys, geese, game, poultry, brawn, meat, pigs, sausages, oysters, pies, puddings, fruit, and punch, all vanished instantly. They stood in the city streets on Christmas morning, where (for the weather was severe) the people made a rough, but brisk and not unpleasant kind of music, in scraping the snow from the pavement in front of their dwellings and from the tops of their houses.

At the same time there emerged from scores of by-streets, lanes, and nameless turnings, innumerable people, carrying their dinners to the bakers' shops. The sight of these poor revellers appeared to interest the Spirit very much, for he stood with Scrooge beside him in a baker's doorway, and taking off the covers as their bearers passed, sprinkled incense on their dinners from his torch. And it was a very uncommon kind of torch, for once or twice when there were angry words between some dinner-carriers who had jostled each other, he shed a few drops of water on them from it, and their good humour was restored directly. For they said, it was a shame to quarrel upon Christmas Day. And so it was! God love it, so it was!

"Is there a peculiar flavour in what you sprinkle from your torch?" asked Scrooge.

"There is. My own."

"Would it apply to any kind of dinner on this day?" asked Scrooge.

"To any kindly given. To a poor one most."

They went on, invisible, as they had been before, into the suburbs of the town, straight to Scrooge's clerk's, and on the threshold of the door the Spirit smiled, and stopped to bless Bob Cratchit's dwelling with the sprinklings of his torch. Think of that! Bob had but fifteen "Bob" a week himself; he pocketed on

Saturdays but fifteen copies of his Christian name; and yet the Ghost of Christmas Present blessed his four-roomed house!

Then up rose Mrs. Cratchit, Cratchit's wife, dressed out but poorly in a twice-turned gown, but brave in ribbons, which are cheap and make a goodly show for sixpence; and she laid the cloth, assisted by Belinda Cratchit, second of her daughters, also brave in ribbons; while Master Peter Cratchit plunged a fork into the saucepan of potatoes, and getting the corners of his monstrous shirt collar (Bob's private property, conferred upon his son and heir in honour of the day) into his mouth, rejoiced to find himself so gallantly attired, and yearned to show his linen in the fashionable Parks. And now two smaller Cratchits, boy and girl, came tearing in, screaming that outside the baker's they had smelt the goose, and known it for their own; and basking in luxurious thoughts of sage and onion, these young Cratchits danced about the table, and exalted Master Peter Cratchit to the skies; while he blew the fire, until the slow potatoes, bubbling up, knocked loudly at the saucepan-lid to be let out and peeled.

"What has ever got your precious father then?" said Mrs. Cratchit. "And your brother, Tiny Tim! And Martha warn't as late last Christmas Day by half-an-hour!"

"Here's Martha, mother!" said a girl, appearing as she spoke.

"Why, bless your heart alive, my dear, how late you are!" said Mrs. Cratchit, kissing her a dozen times, and taking off her shawl and bonnet for her with officious zeal.

"We'd a deal of work to finish up last night," replied the girl, "and had to clear away this morning, mother!"

"Well! Never mind, so long as you are come," said Mrs. Cratchit. "Sit ye down before the fire, my dear, and have a warm, Lord bless ye!"

"No, no! There's father coming," cried the two young Cratchits, who were everywhere at once. "Hide, Martha, hide!"

So Martha hid herself, and in came little Bob, the father, with his threadbare clothes darned up and brushed, to look seasonable; and Tiny Tim upon his shoulder. Alas for Tiny Tim, he bore a little crutch, and had his limbs supported by an iron frame!

"Why, where's our Martha?" cried Bob Cratchit, looking round.

"Not coming," said Mrs. Cratchit.

"Not coming!" said Bob with a sudden declension in his high spirits; for he had been Tim's blood horse all the way from church, and had come home rampant. "Not coming upon Christmas Day!"

Martha didn't like to see him disappointed, if it were only a joke; so she came out prematurely from behind the closet door, and ran into his arms, while the two young Cratchits hustled Tiny Tim, and bore him off into the wash-house, that he might hear the pudding singing in the copper.

"And how did little Tim behave?" asked Mrs. Cratchit, when she had rallied Bob on his credulity, and Bob had hugged his daughter to his heart's content.

"As good as gold," said Bob, "and better. Somehow he gets thoughtful, sitting by himself so much, and thinks the strangest things you ever heard. He told me, coming home, that he hoped the people saw him in the church, because he was a cripple, and it might be pleasant to them to remember upon Christmas Day, who made lame beggars walk and blind men see."

Bob's voice was tremulous when he told them this, and trembled more when he said that Tiny Tim was growing strong and hearty.

His active little crutch was heard upon the floor, and back came Tiny Tim before another word was spoken, escorted by his brother and sister to his stool before the fire; and while Bob turning up his cuffs—as if, poor fellow, they were capable of being made more shabby—compounded some hot mixture in a jug with gin and lemons, and stirred it round and round and put it on the hob to simmer; Master Peter and the two ubiquitous young Cratchits went to fetch the goose, with which they soon returned in high procession.

Such a bustle ensued that you might have thought a goose the rarest of all birds; a feathered phenomenon, to which a black swan was a matter of course—and in truth it was something very like it in that house. Mrs. Cratchit made the gravy (ready beforehand in a little saucepan) hissing hot; Master Peter mashed the potatoes with incredible vigor; Miss Belinda sweetened up the apple-sauce; Martha dusted the hot plates; Bob took Tiny Tim beside him in a tiny corner at the table; the two young Cratchits set chairs for everybody, not forgetting themselves, and mounting guard upon their posts, crammed spoons into their mouths, lest they should shriek for goose before their turn came to be helped. At last the dishes were set on, and grace was said. It was succeeded by a breathless pause, as Mrs. Cratchit, looking slowly all along the carving-knife, prepared to plunge it in the breast; but when she did, and when the long-expected gush of stuffing issued forth, one murmur of delight arose all round the board, and even Tiny Tim, excited by the two young Cratchits, beat on the table with the handle of his knife, and feebly cried Hurrah!

There never was such a goose. Bob said he didn't believe there ever was such a goose cooked. Its tenderness and flavour, size and cheapness, were the themes of universal admiration. Eked out by apple-sauce and mashed potatoes, it was a sufficient dinner for the whole family; indeed, as Mrs. Cratchit said with great delight (surveying one small atom of a bone upon the dish), they hadn't ate it all at last! Yet everyone had had enough, and the youngest Cratchits in particular, were steeped in sage and onion to the eyebrows! But now, the plates being changed by Miss Belinda, Mrs. Cratchit left the room alone—too nervous to bear witnesses—to take the pudding up and bring it in.

Hallo! A great deal of steam! The pudding was out of the copper. A smell like a washing day! That was the cloth. A smell like an eating-house and a pastry cook's next door to each other, with a laundress's next door to that! That was the pudding! In half a minute Mrs. Cratchit entered—flushed, but smiling proudly —with the pudding, like a speckled cannon-ball, so hard and firm, blazing in half of half-a-quartern of ignited brandy, and bedight with Christmas holly stuck into the top. Oh, a wonderful pudding! Bob Cratchit said, and calmly too, that he regarded it as the greatest success achieved by Mrs. Cratchit since their marriage.

At last the dinner was all done, the cloth was cleared, the hearth swept, and the fire made up. The compound in the jug being tasted, and considered perfect, apples and oranges were put upon the table, and a shovelful of chestnuts on the fire. Then all the Cratchit family drew round the hearth, in what Bob Cratchit called a circle, meaning half a one; and at Bob Cratchit's elbow stood the family display of glass. Two tumblers, and a custard-cup without a handle.

These held the hot stuff from the jug, however, as well as golden goblets would have done; and Bob served it out with beam-

ing looks, while the chestnuts on the fire sputtered and cracked noisily. Then Bob proposed:

"A merry Christmas to us all, my dears. God bless us!"

Which all the family re-echoed.

"God bless us every one!" said Tiny Tim, the last of all.

"Spirit," said Scrooge, with an interest he had never felt before, "tell me if Tiny Tim will live."

"I see a vacant seat," replied the Ghost, "in the poor chimney-corner, and a crutch without an owner, carefully preserved. If these shadows remain unaltered by the Future, the child will die."

"No, no," said Scrooge. "Oh, no, kind Spirit! say he will be spared."

"If he be like to die, he had better do it, and decrease the surplus population."

Scrooge hung his head to hear his own words quoted by the Spirit, and trembling cast his eyes upon the ground. But he raised them speedily, on hearing his own name.

"Mr. Scrooge!" said Bob; "I'll give you Mr. Scrooge, the Founder of the Feast!"

"The Founder of the Feast indeed!" cried Mrs. Cratchit, reddening. "I wish I had him here. I'd give him a piece of my mind to feast upon, and I hope he'd have a good appetite for it."

"My dear," said Bob, "the children! Christmas Day."

"It should be Christmas Day, I am sure," said she, "on which one drinks the health of such an odious, stingy, hard, unfeeling man as Mr. Scrooge. You know he is, Robert! Nobody knows it better than you do, poor fellow!"

"My dear," was Bob's mild answer, "Christmas Day."

"I'll drink his health for your sake and the Day's," said Mrs. Cratchit, "not for his. Long life to him! A merry Christmas and a happy New Year! He'll be very merry and very happy, I have no doubt!"

The mention of Scrooge's name cast a dark shadow on the party, which was not dispelled for full five minutes.

After it had passed away they were ten times merrier than before, from the mere relief of Scrooge the Baleful being done with. Bob Cratchit told them how he had a situation in his eye, for Master Peter, which would bring in, if obtained, full five-and-sixpence weekly. The two young Cratchits laughed tremendously at the idea of Peter's being a man of business; and Peter himself looked thoughtfully at the fire from between his collars. Martha, who was a poor apprentice at a milliner's, then told them what kind of work she had to do, and how many hours she worked at a stretch, and how she meant to lie abed tomorrow morning for a good long rest; tomorrow being a holiday she passed at home. All this time the chestnuts and the jug went round and round; and by and by they had a song, about a lost child travelling in the snow, from Tiny Tim, who had a plaintive little voice, and sang it very well indeed.

By this time it was getting dark, and snowing pretty heavily, and without any warning from the Ghost the Cratchits faded away. It was a great surprise to Scrooge to hear a hearty laugh. It was a much greater surprise to recognise it as his own nephew's and to find himself in a bright, dry, gleaming room, with the Spirit standing smiling by his side, and looking at that same nephew with approving affability!

"Ha, ha!" laughed Scrooge's nephew. "Ha, ha, ha! He said that Christmas was a humbug, as I live! He believed it too! Ha, ha, ha!"

"More shame for him, Fred!" said Scrooge's niece, indignantly.

She was very pretty; exceedingly pretty. With a dimpled, surprised-looking, capital face; a ripe little mouth, that seemed made to be kissed—as no doubt it was.

"He's a comical old fellow," said Scrooge's nephew, "that's the truth; and not so pleasant as he might be. However, his offences carry their own punishment, and I have nothing to say against him."

"I'm sure he is very rich, Fred. At least you always tell *me* so."

"What of that, my dear!" said Scrooge's nephew. "His wealth is of no use to him. He don't make himself comfortable with it."

"I have no patience with him," observed Scrooge's niece. Scrooge's niece's sisters, and all the other ladies, expressed the same opinion.

"Oh, I have!" said Scrooge's nephew. "I am sorry for him. Who suffers by his ill whims? Himself, always. Here, he takes it into his head to dislike us, and he won't come and dine with us. What's the consequence? He don't lose much of a dinner."

"Indeed, I think he loses a very good dinner," interrupted

Scrooge's niece. Everybody else said the same, and they must be allowed to have been competent judges, because they had just had dinner; and, with the dessert upon the table, were clustered round the fire, by lamplight.

After a while they played at forfeits; for it is good to be children sometimes, and never better than at Christmas, when its mighty Founder was a child himself. Stop! There was first a game at blind-man's-buff. Of course there was. Scrooge's niece was not one of the blind-man's-buff party, but at the game of How, When, and Where, she was very great, and to the secret joy of Scrooge's nephew, beat her sisters hollow. There might have been twenty people there, young and old, but they all played, and so did Scrooge; for wholly forgetting, in the interest he had in what was going on, that his voice made no sound in their ears, he sometimes came out with his guess quite loud, and very often guessed quite right, too.

The Ghost was greatly pleased to find him in this mood, and looked upon him with such favour that he begged like a boy to be allowed to stay until the guests departed. But this the Spirit said could not be done.

"Here is a new game," said Scrooge. "One half-hour, Spirit, only one!"

It was a game called Yes and No, where Scrooge's nephew had to think of something, and the rest must find out what; he only answering to their questions yes or no, as the case was. The brisk fire of questioning to which he was exposed elicited from him that he was thinking of an animal, a live animal, rather a disagreeable animal, a savage animal, an animal that growled and grunted sometimes, and talked sometimes, and lived in London, and walked about the streets, and wasn't made a show of, and wasn't led by anybody, and didn't live in a menagerie, and was never killed in a market. At every fresh question that was put to him, this nephew burst into a fresh roar of laughter; and was so inexpressibly tickled that he was obliged to get up off the sofa and stamp. At last the plump sister, falling into a similar state, cried out:

"I have found it out. I know what it is, Fred! I know what it is!"

"What is it?" cried Fred.

"It's your Uncle Scro-o-o-o-oge!"

Which it certainly was.

"He has given us plenty of merriment, I am sure," said Fred, "and it would be ungrateful not to drink his health. Here is a glass of mulled wine ready to our hand at the moment; and I say, 'Uncle Scrooge!' "

"Well, Uncle Scrooge!" they cried.

Uncle Scrooge had imperceptibly become so gay and light of heart that he would have pledged the unconscious company in return, and thanked them in an audible speech if the Ghost had given him time. But the whole scene passed off in the breath of the last word spoken by his nephew; and he and the Spirit were again upon their travels.

Much they saw, and far they went, and many homes they visited, but always with a happy end.

It was a long night, if it were only a night; but Scrooge had his doubts of this, because while he remained unaltered in his outward form, the Ghost grew older, clearly older.

"Are spirits' lives so short?" asked Scrooge.

"My life upon this globe is very brief," replied the Ghost. "It ends tonight. Hark! The time is drawing near."

The chimes were ringing the three quarters past eleven at that moment.

"Forgive me if I am not justified in what I ask," said Scrooge, looking intently at the Spirit's robe, "but I see something strange, and not belonging to yourself, protruding from your skirts. Is it a foot or a claw?"

"It might be a claw, for the flesh there is upon it," was the Spirit's sorrowful reply. "Look here."

From the foldings of its robe it brought two children; wretched, abject, frightful, hideous, miserable.

They were a boy and a girl. Yellow, meagre, ragged, scowling, wolfish.

No change, no degradation, no perversion of humanity, in any grade, through all the mysteries of wonderful creation, has monsters half so horrible and dread.

"Spirit! are they yours?" Scrooge could say no more.

"They are Man's," said the Spirit, looking down upon them. "This boy is Ignorance. This girl is Want. Beware them both, and all of their degree, but most of all beware this boy, for on his brow I see that written which is Doom, unless the writing be erased."

"Have they no refuge or resource?" cried Scrooge.

"Are there no prisons?" said the Spirit, turning to him for the last time with his own words. "Are there no workhouses?"

The bell struck twelve.

Scrooge looked about him for the Ghost, and saw it not. As the last stroke ceased to vibrate, he remembered the prediction of old Jacob Marley, and lifting up his eyes, beheld a solemn Phantom, draped and hooded, coming, like a mist along the ground, towards him.

Stave Four: THE LAST OF THE SPIRITS

The Phantom slowly, gravely, silently approached. When it came near him, Scrooge bent down upon his knee; for in the very air through which this Spirit moved it seemed to scatter gloom and mystery.

It was shrouded in a deep black garment, which concealed its head, its face, its form, and left nothing of it visible save one outstretched hand.

"I am in the presence of the Ghost of Christmas Yet to Come?" said Scrooge.

The Spirit answered not, but pointed onward with its hand.

"You are about to show me shadows of the things that have not happened, but will happen in the time before us," Scrooge pursued. "Is that so, Spirit?"

The upper portion of the garment was contracted for an instant in its folds, as if the Spirit had inclined its head. That was the only answer he received.

"Lead on!" said Scrooge. "Lead, Spirit!"

They scarcely seemed to enter the city; for the city rather seemed to spring up about them, and encompass them of its own act. But there they were, in the heart of it; on 'Change, amongst the merchants; who hurried up and down, and chinked the money in their pockets, and conversed in groups.

The Spirit stopped beside one little knot of business men. Observing that the hand was pointed to them, Scrooge advanced to listen to their talk.

"No," said a great fat man with a monstrous chin, "I don't know much about it, either way. I only know he's dead."

"When did he die?" inquired another.

"Last night, I believe."

"Why, what was the matter with him?" asked a third. "I thought he'd never die."

"God knows," said the first, with a yawn.

"What has he done with his money?" asked a red-faced gentleman with a pendulous excrescence on the end of his nose, that shook like the gills of a turkey-cock.

"I haven't heard," said the man with the large chin, yawning again. "Left it to his company, perhaps. He hasn't left it to *me*. That's all I know."

This pleasantry was received with a general laugh.

"It's likely to be a very cheap funeral," said the same speaker; "for upon my life I don't know of anybody to go to it."

They left the busy scene, and went into an obscure part of the town, where Scrooge had never penetrated before, although he recognised its situation and its bad repute. The ways were foul and narrow; the shops and houses wretched; the people half-naked, drunken, slipshod, ugly; and the whole quarter reeked with crime, with filth and misery.

Far in this den of infamous resort, there was a low-browed, beetling shop, where iron, old rags, bottles, bones, and greasy offal were bought. Sitting in among the wares he dealt in, by a charcoal stove, made of old bricks, was a gray-haired rascal, nearly seventy years of age, who smoked his pipe in all the luxury of calm retirement.

Scrooge and the Phantom came into the presence of this man, just as a woman with a heavy bundle slunk into the shop. But she had scarcely entered, when another woman, similarly laden, came in too; and she was closely followed by a man in faded black, who was no less startled by the sight of them, than they had been upon the recognition of each other. After a short period of blank astonishment, in which the old man with the pipe had joined them, they all three burst into a laugh.

"Let the charwoman alone to be the first!" cried she who had entered first. "Let the laundress alone to be the second; and let the undertaker's man alone to be the third. Look here, old Joe, here's a chance! If we haven't all three met here without meaning it!"

"You couldn't have met in a better place," said old Joe, removing his pipe from his mouth. "Ha, ha! We're all suitable to our calling, we're well matched. Come into the parlor."

The parlor was the space behind a screen of rags. The old man raked the fire together with an old stair-rod, and having trimmed his smoky lamp (for it was night), with the stem of his pipe, put it in his mouth again.

While he did this, the woman who had already spoken threw her bundle on the floor, looking with a bold defiance at the other two.

The man in faded black produced *his* plunder. It was not extensive. A seal or two, a pencil-case, a pair of sleeve-buttons, and a brooch of no great value, were all. They were severally examined and appraised by old Joe, who chalked the sums he was disposed to give for each, upon the wall, and added them up into a total, when he found there was nothing more to come.

"That's your account," said Joe, "and I wouldn't give another sixpence, if I was to be boiled for not doing it. Who's next?"

Mrs. Dilber was next. Sheets and towels, a little wearing apparel, two old-fashioned silver teaspoons, a pair of sugar-tongs, and a few boots. Her account was stated on the wall in the same manner.

"And now undo *my* bundle, Joe," said the first woman.

Joe went down on his knees for the greater convenience of opening it, and having unfastened a great many knots, dragged out a large and heavy roll of some dark stuff.

"What do you call this?" said Joe. "Bed-curtains! You don't mean to say you took 'em down, rings and all, with him lying there?"

"Yes, I do," replied the woman. "Why not?"

"You were born to make your fortune," said Joe, "and you'll certainly do it."

"I certainly sha'n't hold my hand, when I can get anything in it by reaching it out, for the sake of such a man as he was, I promise you, Joe," returned the woman coolly. "Don't drop that oil upon the blankets, now."

"His blankets?" asked Joe.

"Whose else's do you think?" replied the woman. "He isn't likely to take cold without 'em, I dare say."

"I hope he didn't die of anything catching? Eh?" said old Joe, stopping in his work, and looking up.

"Don't you be afraid of that," returned the woman. "I an't so fond of his company that I'd loiter about him for such things, if he did. Ah! you may look through that shirt till your eyes ache; but you won't find a hole in it, nor a threadbare place. It's the best he had, and a fine one too. They'd have wasted it, if it hadn't been for me."

"What do you call wasting of it?" asked old Joe.

"Putting it on him to be buried in, to be sure," replied the woman, with a laugh. "Somebody was fool enough to do it, but I took it off again. If calico an't good enough for such a purpose, it isn't good enough for anything. It's quite as becoming to the body. He can't look uglier than he did in that one."

Scrooge listened to this dialogue in horror.

"Spirit!" he said, shuddering from head to foot. "I see, I see. The case of this unhappy man might be my own. My life tends that way now. Merciful Heaven, what is this!"

He recoiled in terror, for the scene had changed, and now he almost touched a bed; a bare, uncurtained bed; on which, beneath a ragged sheet, there lay a something covered up, which, though it was dumb, announced itself in awful language.

Scrooge glanced toward the Phantom. Its steady hand was pointed to the head. The cover was so carelessly adjusted that the slightest raising of it, the motion of a finger upon Scrooge's part, would have disclosed the face. He thought of it, felt how easy it would be to do, and longed to do it; but had no more power to withdraw the veil than to dismiss the spectre at his side.

"Spirit!" he said, "this is a fearful place. In leaving it, I shall not leave its lesson, trust me. Let us go!"

Still the Ghost pointed with an unmoved finger to the head.

"If there is any person in the town who feels emotion caused by this man's death," said Scrooge, quite agonised, "show that person to me, Spirit, I beseech you!"

The Phantom spread its dark robe before him for a moment, like a wing; and withdrawing it, revealed a room by daylight, where a mother and her children were.

A knock was heard. She hurried to the door, and met her husband; a man whose face was careworn and depressed, though he was young. There was a remarkable expression in it now; a kind of serious delight of which he felt ashamed, and which he struggled to repress.

He sat down to the dinner that she had been hoarding for him by the fire; and when she asked him faintly what news (which was not until after a long silence), he appeared embarrassed how to answer.

"Is it good," she said, "or bad?"—to help him.

"Bad," he answered.

"We are quite ruined?"

"No. There is hope yet, Caroline."

"If *he* relents," she said, amazed, "there is! Nothing is past hope, if such a miracle has happened."

"He is past relenting," said her husband. "He is dead."

"To whom will our debt be transferred?"

"I don't know. But before that time we shall be ready with the money; and even though we were not, it would be bad fortune indeed to find so merciless a creditor in his successor. We may sleep tonight with light hearts, Caroline!"

Yes. It was a happier house for this man's death! The only emotion that the Ghost could show him, caused by the event, was one of pleasure.

"Let me see some tenderness connected with a death," said Scrooge.

The Ghost conducted him to Bob Cratchit's house; the dwelling he had visited before; and found the mother and the children seated round the fire.

Quiet. Very quiet. The noisy little Cratchits were as still as statues in one corner, and sat looking up at Peter, who had a book before him. The mother and her daughters were engaged in sewing. But surely they were very quiet!

" 'And he took a child and set him in the midst of them.' "

Where had Scrooge heard those words. The boy must have read them out as he and the Spirit crossed the threshold.

The mother laid her work upon the table, and put her hand up to her face.

"The color hurts my eyes," she said.

The color? Ah, poor Tiny Tim!

"They're better now again," said Cratchit's wife. "It makes them weak by candlelight; and I wouldn't show weak eyes to your father when he comes home for the world. It must be near his time."

They were very quiet again. At last she said, and in a steady, cheerful voice, that only faltered once:

"I have known him walk with—I have known him walk with Tiny Tim upon his shoulder, very fast indeed."

"And so have I," cried Peter. "Often."

"But he was very light to carry," she resumed, intent upon her work, "and his father loved him so, that it was no trouble. And there is your father at the door!"

Bob was very cheerful with them. He looked at the work upon the table, and praised the industry and speed of Mrs. Cratchit and the girls. They would be done long before Sunday he said.

"Sunday! You went today, then, Robert?" said his wife.

"Yes, my dear," returned Bob. "I wish you could have gone. It would have done you good to see how green a place it is. But you'll see it often. I promised him that I would walk there on a Sunday. My little, little child!" cried Bob. "My little child!"

He broke down all at once. He couldn't help it. If he could have helped it, he and his child would have been farther apart perhaps than they were.

He left the room, and went upstairs into the room above, which was lighted cheerfully and hung with Christmas. There was a chair set close beside the child, and there were signs of someone having been there lately. Poor Bob sat down in it, and when he had thought a little and composed himself, he kissed the little face. He was reconciled to what had happened, and went down again quite happy.

Spirit of Tiny Tim, thy childish essence was from God!

"Spectre," said Scrooge, "something informs me that our parting moment is at hand. Tell me what man that was whom we saw lying dead?"

The Ghost of Christmas Yet To Come conveyed him to a churchyard. Here, then, the wretched man whose name he had now to learn, lay underneath the ground.

The Spirit stood among the graves, and pointed down to One.

Scrooge crept towards it, trembling as he went; and following the finger, read upon the stone of the neglected grave his own name, EBENEZER SCROOGE.

"Am *I* that man who lay upon the bed?" he cried, upon his knees.

The finger pointed from the grave to him, and back again.

"No, Spirit! Oh no, no! Hear me! I am not the man I was. Why show me this, if I am past all hope!"

For the first time the hand appeared to shake.

"Good Spirit," he pursued, as down upon the ground he fell before it, "assure me that I yet may change these shadows you have shown me, by an altered life!"

The kind hand trembled.

"I will honor Christmas in my heart, and try to keep it all the year. I will live in the Past, the Present, and the Future. The Spirits of all Three shall strive within me. I will not shut out the lessons that they teach. Oh, tell me I may sponge away the writing on this stone!"

In his agony, he caught the spectral hand. It sought to free itself but he was strong in his entreaty, and detained it. The Spirit, stronger yet, repulsed him.

Holding up his hands in a last prayer to have his fate reversed, he saw an alteration in the Phantom's hood and dress. It shrunk, collapsed, and dwindled down into a bedpost.

Stave Five: THE END OF IT

Yes! and the bedpost was his own. The bed was his own, the room was his own. Best and happiest of all, the Time before him was his own, to make amends in!

"I will live in the Past, the Present, and the Future!" Scrooge repeated, as he scrambled out of bed. "The Spirits of all Three shall strive within me.

"They are not torn down," cried Scrooge, folding one of his bed-curtains in his arms. "They are here, I am here—the shadows of the things that would have been may be dispelled. They will be. I know they will!"

"I don't know what to do!" cried Scrooge, laughing and crying in the same breath. "I am as light as a feather, I am as happy as an angel. I am as giddy as a drunken man. A Merry Christmas to

everybody! A happy New Year to all the world. Hallo here!
Whoop! Hallo!"

He had frisked into the sitting-room, and was now standing
there, perfectly winded.

"I don't know what day of the month it is!" said Scrooge. "I
don't know how long I've been among the spirits. I don't know
anything. I'm quite a baby. Never mind. I don't care. I'd rather
be a baby. Hallo! Whoop! Hallo here!"

Running to the window, he opened it, and put out his head. No
fog, no mist; clear, bright, jovial, stirring, cold; cold, piping for
the blood to dance to. Oh, glorious! Glorious!

"What's today!" cried Scrooge, calling downward to a boy in
Sunday clothes, who perhaps had loitered in to look about him.

"Today!" replied the boy. "Why, Christmas Day."

"It's Christmas Day!" said Scrooge to himself. "I haven't
missed it. The Spirits have done it all in one night. Hallo, my
fine fellow!"

"Hallo!" returned the boy.

"Do you know the poulterer's, in the next street but one, at the
corner?" Scrooge inquired.

"I should hope I did," replied the lad.

"An intelligent boy!" said Scrooge. "A remarkable boy! Do you
know whether they've sold the prize turkey that was hanging up
there?—Not the little prize turkey: the big one?"

"It's hanging there now," replied the boy.

"Is it?" said Scrooge. "Go and buy it, and tell 'em to bring it
here, that I may give them the direction where to take it. Come
back with the man, and I'll give you a shilling. Come back with
him in less than five minutes and I'll give you half-a-crown!"

The boy was off like a shot.

"I'll send it to Bob Cratchit's!" whispered Scrooge, rubbing his
hands, and splitting with a laugh. "He sha'n't know who sends it.
It's twice the size of Tiny Tim."

The hand in which he wrote the address was not a steady one,
but write it he did, somehow, and went downstairs to open the
street door, ready for the coming of the poulterer's man. As he
stood there, waiting his arrival, the knocker caught his eye.

"I shall love it, as long as I live!" cried Scrooge, patting it with his hand. "It's a wonderful knocker!—Here's the turkey. Hallo! Whoop! How are you? Merry Christmas!"

It *was* a turkey! He never could have stood upon his legs, that bird. He would have snapped 'em short off in a minute, like sticks of sealing wax.

"Why, it's impossible to carry that to Camden Town," said Scrooge. "You must have a cab."

The chuckle with which he said this, and the chuckle with which he paid for the turkey, and the chuckle with which he paid for the cab, and the chuckle with which he recompensed the boy, were only to be exceeded by the chuckle with which he sat down breathless in his chair again, and chuckled till he cried.

He dressed himself "all in his best," and at last got out into the streets. He had not gone far when coming on towards him he beheld the portly gentleman who had walked into his counting-house the day before.

"My dear sir," said Scrooge, quickening his pace and taking the old gentleman by both his hands. "How do you do? I hope you succeeded yesterday. It was very kind of you. A merry Christmas to you, sir!"

"Mr. Scrooge?"

"Yes," said Scrooge. "That is my name, and I fear it may not be pleasant to you. Allow me to ask your pardon. And will you have the goodness"—here Scrooge whispered in his ear.

"Lord bless me!" cried the gentleman, as if his breath were taken away. "My dear Mr. Scrooge, are you serious?"

"If you please," said Scrooge. "Not a farthing less. A great many back-payments are included in it, I assure you. Will you do me that favour?"

"My dear sir," said the other, shaking hands with him. "I don't know what to say to such munifi ——"

"Don't say anything, please," retorted Scrooge. "Come and see me. Will you come and see me?"

"I will!" cried the old gentleman. And it was clear that he meant to do it.

"Thank'ee," said Scrooge. "I am much obliged to you. Bless you!"

He went to church, and walked about the streets, and watched the people hurrying to and fro, and patted children on the head, and questioned beggars, and looked down into the kitchens of houses, and up to the windows, and found that everything could yield him pleasure. He had never dreamed that any walk—that anything—could give him so much happiness. In the afternoon he turned his steps towards his nephew's house.

He passed the door a dozen times, before he had the courage to go up and knock. But he made a dash and did it:

"Is your master at home, my dear?" said Scrooge to the girl. Nice girl! Very.

"He's in the dining-room, sir, along with mistress."

He turned the dining-room lock gently, and sidled his face in, round the door.

"Fred!" said Scrooge.

"Why, bless my soul!" cried Fred. "Who's that?"

"It's I. Your uncle Scrooge. I have come to dinner. Will you let me in, Fred?"

Let him in! It is a mercy he didn't shake his arm off. He was at home in five minutes. Nothing could be heartier. His niece looked just the same. So did the plump sister, when *she* came. So did every one when *they* came. Wonderful party, wonderful games, wonderful unanimity, won-der-ful happiness!

But he was early at the office next morning. Oh, he was early there. If he could only be there first, and catch Bob Cratchit coming late! That was the thing he had set his heart upon.

And he did it; yes, he did! The clock struck nine. No Bob. A quarter past. No Bob. He was full eighteen minutes and a half behind his time.

"Hallo," growled Scrooge, in his accustomed voice, as near as he could feign it. "What do you mean by coming here at this time of day?"

"I am very sorry, sir," said Bob. "I *am* behind my time."

"You are?" repeated Scrooge. "Yes. I think you are. Step this way, sir, if you please."

"It's only once a year, sir," pleaded Bob. "It shall not be repeated. I was making rather merry yesterday, sir."

"Now, I'll tell you what, my friend," said Scrooge. "I am not going to stand this sort of thing any longer. And therefore," he continued, leaping from his stool and giving Bob such a dig in the waistcoat that he staggered back into the Tank again; "and therefore I am about to raise your salary!"

Bob trembled, and got a little nearer to the ruler. He had a momentary idea of knocking Scrooge down with it, holding him, and calling to the people in the court for help and a straitwaistcoat.

"A merry Christmas, Bob!" said Scrooge, with an earnestness that could not be mistaken, as he clapped him on the back. "A merrier Christmas, Bob, my good fellow, than I have given you for many a year! I'll raise your salary, and endeavor to assist your struggling family, and we will discuss your affairs this very afternoon, over a Christmas bowl of smoking bishop, Bob! Make up the fires, and buy another coal-scuttle before you dot another i, Bob Cratchit!"

Scrooge was better than his word. He did it all, and infinitely more; and to Tiny Tim, who did NOT die, he was a second father. He became as good a friend, as good a master, and as good a man, as the good old city knew. Some people laughed to see the alteration in him, but he let them laugh, and little heeded them, for he was wise enough to know that nothing ever happened on this globe, for good, at which some people did not have their fill of laughter in the outset; and knowing that such as these would be blind anyway, he thought it quite as well that they should wrinkle up their eyes in grins, as have the malady in less attractive forms. His own heart laughed; and that was quite enough for him.

He had no further intercourse with Spirits, but lived upon the Total Abstinence Principle, ever afterwards; and it was always said of him, that he knew how to keep Christmas well, if any man alive possessed the knowledge. May that be truly said of us, and all of us! And so, as Tiny Tim observed, God bless Us, Every One!

The Candle in the Forest

By Temple Bailey

THE Small Girl's mother was saying, "The onions will be silver, and the carrots will be gold ——"

"And the potatoes will be ivory," said the Small Girl, and they laughed together.

The Small Girl's mother had a big white bowl in her lap and she was cutting up vegetables. The onions were the hardest, because one cried a little over them.

"But our tears will be pearls," said the Small Girl's mother, and they laughed at that and dried their eyes, and found the carrots much easier, and the potatoes the easiest of them all.

Then the Next-Door-Neighbor came in and said, "What are you doing?"

"We are making a beefsteak pie for our Christmas dinner," said the Small Girl's mother.

"And the onions are silver, and the carrots gold, and the potatoes ivory," said the Small Girl.

"I am sure I don't know what you are talking about," said the Next-Door-Neighbor. "We are going to have turkey for Christmas, and oysters and cranberries and celery."

The Small Girl laughed and clapped her hands. "But we are going to have a Christmas pie—and the onions are silver and the carrots gold ——"

"You said that once," said the Next-Door-Neighbor, "and I should think you'd know they weren't anything of the kind."

"But they *are*," said the Small Girl, all shining eyes and rosy cheeks.

"Run along, darling," said the Small Girl's mother, "and find poor Pussy Purr-up. He's out in the cold. And you can put on your red sweater and red cap."

So the Small Girl hopped away like a happy robin, and the Next-Door-Neighbor said:

"She is old enough to know that onions aren't silver."

"But they are," said the Small Girl's mother, "and the carrots are gold, and the potatoes are ——"

The Next-Door-Neighbor's face was flaming.

"If you say that again, I'll scream. It sounds silly to me."

"But it isn't in the least silly," said the Small Girl's mother, and her eyes were as blue as sapphires and as clear as the sea; "it is sensible. When people are poor, they have to make the most of little things."

The lips of the Next-Door-Neighbor were folded in a thin line. "If you had acted like a sensible creature, I shouldn't have asked you for the rent."

The Small Girl's mother was silent for a moment, then she said: "I am sorry—it ought to be sensible to make the best of things."

"Well," said the Next-Door-Neighbor, sitting down in a chair with a very stiff back, "a beefsteak pie is a beefsteak pie. And I wouldn't teach a child to call it anything else."

"I haven't taught her to call it anything else. I was only trying to make her feel that it was something fine and splendid for Christmas day, so I said that the onions were silver ——"

"Don't say that again," snapped the Next-Door-Neighbor, "and I want the rent as soon as possible."

With that, she flung up her head and marched out of the front door, and it slammed behind her and made wild echoes in the little house.

And the Small Girl's mother stood there alone in the middle of the floor, and her eyes were like the sea in a storm.

But presently the door opened, and the Small Girl, looking like a red-breast robin, hopped in, and after her came a great black cat with his tail in the air, and he said "Purr-up," which gave him his name.

And the Small Girl said out of the things she had been thinking, "Mother, why don't we have turkey?"

The clear look came back into the eyes of the Small Girl's mother, and she said, "Because we are content."

And the Small Girl said, "What is 'content'?"

And her mother said: "It is making the best of what God gives us. And our best for Christmas day, my darling, is a beefsteak pie."

So she kissed the Small Girl, and they finished peeling the vegetables, and then they put them with the pound of steak to simmer on the back of the stove.

After that, the Small Girl had her supper of bread and milk, and Pussy Purr-up had milk in a saucer on the hearth, and the Small Girl climbed up in her mother's lap and said:

"Tell me a story."

But the Small Girl's mother said, "Won't it be nicer to talk about Christmas presents?"

And the Small Girl sat up and said, "Let's."

And the mother said, "Let's tell each other what we'd rather have in the whole wide world ———"

"Oh, let's," said the Small Girl. "And I'll tell you first that I want a doll—and I want it to have a pink dress—and I want it to have eyes that open and shut—and I want it to have shoes and stockings—and I want it to have curly hair ———"

She had to stop, because she didn't have any breath left in her body, and when she got her breath back, she said, "Now, what do you want, Mother—more than anything else in the whole wide world?"

"Well," said her mother, "I want a chocolate mouse."

"Oh," said the Small Girl, scornfully, "I shouldn't think you'd want that."

"Why not?"

"Because a chocolate mouse—why, a chocolate mouse isn't anything."

"Oh! yes, it is," said the Small Girl's mother. "A chocolate mouse is Dickory-Dock, and Pussy-Cat-Pussy-Cat-Where-Have-You-Been—and it's Three-Blind-Mice—and it's A-Frog-He-Would-a-Wooing-Go—and it's ———"

The Small Girl's eyes were dancing. "Oh, tell me about it ———"

And her mother said: "Well, the mouse in Dickory-Dock ran *up* the clock, and the mouse in Pussy-Cat-Pussy-Cat was frightened *under* a chair, and the mice in Three-Blind-Mice ran *after* the farmer's wife, and the mouse in A-Frog-He-Would-a-Wooing-Go went *down* the throat of the crow ———"

And the Small Girl said, "Could a chocolate mouse do all that?"

"Well," said the Small Girl's mother, "we could put him *on* the clock, and *under* a chair, and cut his tail *off* with a carving-knife, and at the very last we could eat him *up* like a crow."

The Small girl shivered deliciously. "And he wouldn't be a real mouse."

"No, just a chocolate one, with cream inside."

"Do you think I'll get one for Christmas?"

"I'm not sure."

"Would he be nicer than a doll?"

The Small Girl's mother hesitated, then told the truth. "My darling—Mother saved up the money for a doll, but the Next-Door-Neighbor wants the rent."

"Hasn't Daddy any more money?"

"Poor Daddy has been sick so long."

"But he's well now."

"I know. But he has to pay money for doctors, and money for medicine, and money for your red sweater, and money for milk for Pussy-Purr-up, and money for our beefsteak pie."

"The Boy-Next-Door says we're poor, Mother."

"We are rich, my darling. We have love, and each other, and Pussy-Purr-up ——"

"His mother won't let him have a cat," said the Small Girl, with her mind still on the Boy-Next-Door, "but he's going to have a radio."

"Would you rather have a radio than Pussy-Purr-up?"

The Small Girl gave a crow of derision. "I'd rather have Pussy-Purr-up than anything else in the whole wide world."

At that, the great cat, who had been sitting on the hearth with his paws tucked under him and his eyes like moons, stretched out his satin-shining length, and jumped up on the arm of the chair beside the Small Girl and her mother, and began to sing a song that was like a mill-wheel away off. He purred so long and so loud that at last the Small Girl grew drowsy.

"Tell me some more about the chocolate mouse," she said, and nodded, and slept.

The Small Girl's mother carried her into another room, put her to bed, and came back to the kitchen—and it was full of shadows.

But she did not let herself sit among them. She wrapped herself in a great cape and went out into the cold dusk, with a sweep of wind; heavy clouds overhead; and a band of dull orange showing back of the trees, where the sun had burned down.

*   *   *   *   *

She went straight from her little house to the big house of the Next-Door-Neighbor and rang the bell at the back entrance. A maid let her into the kitchen, and there was the Next-Door-Neighbor, and the two women who worked for her, and a Daughter-in-Law who had come to spend Christmas. The great range was glowing, and things were simmering, and things were stewing, and things were steaming, and things were baking, and things were boiling, and things were broiling, and there was a fragrance of a thousand delicious dishes in the air.

And the Next-Door-Neighbor said: "We are trying to get as much done as possible tonight. We are having twelve people for Christmas dinner tomorrow."

And the Daughter-in-Law, who was all dressed up and had an apron tied about her, said in a sharp voice, "I can't see why you don't let your maids work for you."

And the Next-Door-Neighbor said: "I have always worked. There is no excuse for laziness."

And the Daughter-in-Law said: "I'm not lazy, if that's what you mean. And we'll never have any dinner if I have to cook it," and away she went out of the kitchen with tears of rage in her eyes.

And the Next-Door-Neighbor said, "If she hadn't gone when she did, I should have told her to go," and there was rage in her eyes, but no tears.

She took her hands out of the pan of bread crumbs and sage, which she was mixing for the stuffing, and said to the Small Girl's mother:

"Did you come to pay the rent?"

The Small Girl's mother handed her the money, and the Next-Door-Neighbor went upstairs to write a receipt. Nobody asked the Small Girl's mother to sit down, so she stood in the middle of the floor, and sniffed the entrancing fragrances, and looked at the mountain of food which would have served her small family for a month.

While she waited, the Boy-Next-Door came in and he said, "Are you the Small Girl's mother?"

"Yes."

"Are you going to have a tree?"

"Yes."

"Do you want to see mine?"

"It would be wonderful."

So he led her down a long passage to a great room, and there was a tree which touched the ceiling, and on the very top branches and on all the other branches were myriads of little lights which shone like stars and there were gold balls and silver ones, and gold bells and silver ones, and red and blue and green bells—and under the tree and on it were toys for boys and toys for girls, and one of the toys was a doll in a pink dress!

At that the heart of the Small Girl's mother tightened, and she was glad she wasn't a thief or she would have snatched at the pink doll when the boy wasn't looking and hidden it under her cape and run away with it!

The Boy-Next-Door was saying: "It's the finest tree anybody has around here. But Dad and Mother don't know that I've seen it."

"Oh, don't they?" said the Small Girl's mother.

"No," said the Boy-Next-Door, with a wide grin, "and it's fun to fool 'em."

"Is it?" said the Small Girl's mother. "Now, do you know, I should think the very nicest thing in the whole wide world would be *not* to have seen the tree."

The Boy-Next-Door stared and said, "Why?"

"Because," said the Small Girl's mother, "the nicest thing in the world would be to have somebody tie a handkerchief around your eyes, as tight as tight, and then to have somebody take your hand and lead you in and out and in and out and in and out until you didn't know where you were, and then to have them untie the handkerchief—and there would be the tree—all shining and splendid ——"

She stopped, but her singing voice seemed to echo and re-echo in a great room.

The boy's staring eyes had a new look in them.

"Did anybody ever tie a handkerchief over your eyes?"

"Oh yes ——"

"And lead you in and out, and in and out?"

"Yes."

"Well, nobody does things like that in our house. They think it's silly."

The Small Girl's mother laughed and her laugh tinkled like a bell. "Do you think it is silly?"

He was eager. "No, I don't."

She held out her hand to him. "Will you come and see our tree?"

"Tonight?"

"No, tomorrow morning—early."

"Before breakfast?"

She nodded.

"Gee, I'd like it."

So that was a bargain, with a quick squeeze of their hands on it. And the Small Girl's mother went back to the kitchen, and the Next-Door-Neighbor came down with the receipt, and the Small Girl's mother went out of the back door and found that the orange band which had burned on the horizon was gone, and that there was just the wind and the sighing of the trees.

Two men passed her on the brick walk which led to the house, and one of the men was saying:

"If you'd only be fair to me, Father."

And the other man said, "All you want of me is money."

"You taught me that, Father."

"Blame it on me ——"

"You are to blame. You and Mother—did you ever show me the finer things?"

Their angry voices seemed to beat against the noise of the wind and the sighing trees, so that the Small Girl's mother shivered and drew her cape around her, and ran on as fast as she could to her little house.

There were all the shadows to meet her, but she did not sit among them. She made coffee and a dish of milk toast, and set the toast in the oven to keep hot, and then she stood at the window watching. At last she saw through the darkness what looked like a star low down, and she knew that the star was a lantern, and she ran and opened the door wide.

And the young husband set the lantern down on the threshold, and took her in his arms, and said, "The sight of you is more than food and drink."

When he said that, she knew he had had a hard day, but her heart leaped, because she knew that what he had said of her was true.

Then they went into the house together, and she set the food before him. And that he might forget his hard day, she told him of her own. And when she came to the part about the Next-Door-Neighbor and the rent, she said:

"I am telling you this because it has a happy ending."

And he put his hands over hers and said, "Everything with you has a happy ending."

"Well, *this* is a happy ending," said the Small Girl's mother, with all the sapphire in her eyes emphasizing it. "Because when I went over to pay the rent I was feeling how poor we were, and wishing that I had a pink doll for baby, and books for you, and—and—and a magic carpet to carry us away from work and worry. And then I went into the kitchen of the big house, and there was everything delicious and delectable, and then I went into the parlor and saw the tree—with everything hanging on it that was glittering and gorgeous—and then I came home"—her breath was quick and her lips smiling—"I came home—and I was glad I lived in my little house."

"What made you glad, dearest?"

"Oh, love is here; and hate is there, and a boy's deceit, and a man's injustice. They were saying sharp things to each other—and—and—their dinner will be a—stalled ox. And in my little house is the faith of a child in the goodness of God and the bravery of a man who fought for his country ——"

She was in his arms now.

"And the blessing of a woman who has never known defeat." His voice broke on the words.

In that moment it seemed as if the wind stopped blowing and as if the trees stopped sighing and as if there was the sound of a heavenly host singing ——

The Small Girl's mother and the Small Girl's father sat up very late that night. They popped a great bowlful of crisp snowy corn and made it into balls. They boiled sugar and molasses and

cracked nuts and made candy of them. They cut funny little Christmas fairies out of paper and painted their jackets bright red, with
round silver buttons of the tin foil that came on a cream cheese.
And then they put the balls and the candy and the painted fairies
and a long red candle in a big basket and set it away. And the
Small Girl's mother brought out the chocolate mouse.

"We will put this on the clock," she said, "where her eyes will
rest on it the first thing in the morning."

So they put it there and it seemed as natural as life, so that
Pussy Purr-up positively licked his chops and sat in front of the
clock as if to keep his eye on the chocolate mouse.

And the Small Girl's mother said, "She was lovely about giving
up the doll, and she will love the tree."

"We'll have to get up very early," said the Small Girl's father.

"And you'll have to run ahead and light the candle."

Well, they got up before the dawn the next morning, and so did
the Boy-Next-Door. He was there on the step, waiting, blowing
his hands and beating them quite like the poor little boys in a
Christmas story, who haven't any mittens.

But he wasn't a poor little boy, and he had so many pairs of
fur-trimmed gloves that he didn't know what to do with them,
but he had left the house in such a hurry that he had forgotten
to put them on.

So there he stood on the front step of the little house, blowing
on his hands and beating them. And it was dark, with a sort of
pale shine in the heavens, which didn't seem to come from the stars
or to herald the dawn; it was just a mystical silver glow that set
the boy's heart to beating.

He had never been out alone like this. He had always stayed
in his warm bed until somebody called him, and then he had
waited until they called again, and then he had dressed and gone
down to breakfast, where his father scolded because he was late,
and his mother scolded because he ate too fast. But this day had
begun with adventure, and for the first time, under that silver
sky, he felt the thrill of it.

Then suddenly someone came around the corner—someone tall
and thin, with a cap on his head and an empty basket in his hands.

"Hello," he said. "A merry Christmas."

It was the Small Girl's father, and he put the key in the lock, and went in, and turned on a light, and there was the table set for four.

And the Small Girl's father said: "You see we have set a place for you. We must eat something before we go out."

And the Boy said: "Are we going out? I came to see the tree."

"We are going out to see the tree."

Before the Boy-Next-Door could ask any questions the Small Girl's mother appeared with her finger on her lips and said: "Sh-sh," and then she began to recite in a hushed voice,

"Hickory-Dickory-Dock ——"

Then there was a little cry and the sound of dancing feet and the Small Girl in a red dressing-gown came flying in.

"Oh, Mother, the mouse is *on* the clock! The mouse is *on* the clock!"

Well, it seemed to the Boy-Next-Door that he had never seen anything so exciting as the things that followed. The chocolate mouse went *up* the clock and *under* the chair—and would have had its tail cut *off* except that the Small Girl begged to save it.

"I want to keep it as it is, Mother."

And playing this game as if it were the most important thing in the whole wide world were the Small Girl's mother and the Small Girl's father, all laughing and flushed, and chanting the quaint old words to the quaint old music.

The Boy-Next-Door held his breath for fear he would wake up from this entrancing dream and find himself in his own big house, alone in his puffy bed, or eating breakfast with his stodgy parents who never had played with him in his life. He found himself laughing, too, and flushed and happy, and trying to sing in his funny boy's voice:

"Heigh-o, says Anthony Rowley!"

The Small Girl absolutely refused to eat the mouse. "He's my darling Christmas mouse, Mother."

So her mother said, "Well, I'll put him on the clock again, where Pussy-Purr-up can't get him while we are out."

"Oh, are we going out?" said the Small Girl, round-eyed.

"Yes."

"Where are we going?"

"To find Christmas."

That was all the Small Girl's mother would tell. So they had breakfast, and everything tasted perfectly delicious to the Boy-Next-Door. But first they bowed their heads, and the Small Girl's father said:

"Dear Christ-Child, on this Christmas morning, bless these children, and help us all to keep our hearts young and full of love for Thee."

The Boy-Next-Door, when he lifted his head, had a funny feeling as if he wanted to cry, and yet it was a lovely feeling, all warm and comfortable.

For breakfast they each had a great baked apple, and great slices of sweet bread and butter, and great glasses of milk, and as soon as they had finished, away they went, out of the door and down into the wood back of the house, and when they were deep in the wood, the Small Girl's father took out of his pocket a little flute and began to play, and he played thin piping tunes that went flittering around among the trees, and the Small Girl hummed the tunes, and her mother hummed the tunes until it sounded like singing bees, and their feet fairly danced, and the boy found himself humming and dancing with them.

Then suddenly the piping ceased, and a hush fell over the wood. It was so still that they could almost hear each other breathe —so still that when a light flamed suddenly in that open space it burned without a flicker.

The light came from a red candle that was set in the top of a small living tree. It was the only light on the tree, but it showed the snowy balls, and the small red fairies whose coats had silver buttons.

"It's our tree, my darling," he heard the Small Girl's mother saying.

Suddenly it seemed to the boy that his heart would burst in his breast. He wanted some one to speak to him like that. The Small Girl sat high on her father's shoulder, and her father held her mother's hand. It was like a chain of gold, their holding hands like that and loving each other ——

The boy reached out and touched the woman's hand. She looked down at him and drew him close. He felt warmed and comforted. The red candle burning there in the darkness was like some sacred fire of friendship. He wished that it would never go out, that he might stand there watching it, with his small cold hand in the clasp of the Small Girl's mother.

*   *   *   *   *

It was late when the Boy-Next-Door got back to his own house. But he had not been missed. Everybody was up, and everybody was angry. The Daughter-in-Law had declared the night before that she would not stay another day beneath that roof, and off she had gone with her young husband, and her little girl, who was to have had the pink doll on the tree.

"And good riddance," said the Next-Door-Neighbor.

But she ate no breakfast, and she went out to the kitchen and worked with her maids to get the dinner ready, and there were covers laid for nine instead of twelve.

And the Next-Door-Neighbor kept saying, "Good riddance— good riddance," and not once did she say, "A merry Christmas."

But the Boy-Next-Door held something in his heart that was

warm and glowing like the candle in the forest, and so he came to his mother and said:

"May I have the pink doll?"

She spoke frowningly, "What does a boy want of a doll?"

"I'd like to give it to the little girl next door."

"Do you think I buy dolls to give away in charity?"

"Well, they gave me a Christmas present."

"What did they give you?"

He opened his hand and showed a little flute tied with a gay red ribbon. He lifted it to his lips and blew on it, a thin piping tune ——

"Oh, that," said the mother, scornfully. "Why, that's nothing but a reed from the pond!"

But the boy knew that it was more than that. It was a magic pipe that made you dance, and made your heart warm and happy.

So he said again, "I'd like to give her the doll," and he reached out his little hand and touched his mother's—and his eyes were wistful.

His mother's own eyes softened—she had lost one son that day —and she said, "Oh, well, do as you please," and went back to the kitchen.

The Boy-Next-Door ran into the great room and took the doll from the tree, and wrapped her in paper, and flew out of the door and down the brick walk and straight into the little house.

When the door was opened, he saw that his friends were just sitting down to dinner—and there was the beefsteak pie all brown and piping hot, with a wreath of holly, and the Small Girl was saying,

"And the onions were silver, and the carrots gold ——"

The Boy-Next-Door went up to the Small Girl and said:

"I've brought you a present."

With his eyes all lighted up, he took off the paper in which it was wrapped, and there was the doll, in rosy frills, with eyes that opened and shut and shoes and stockings and curly hair that was bobbed and beautiful.

And the Small Girl, in a whirlwind of happiness, said, "Is it really *my* doll?"

And the Boy-Next-Door felt very shy and happy, and he said, "Yes."

And the Small Girl's mother said, "It was a beautiful thing to do," and she bent and kissed him.

Again that bursting feeling came into the boy's heart, and he lifted his face to hers and said, "May I come sometimes and be your boy?"

And she said, "Yes."

And when at last he went away, she stood in the door and watched him, such a little lad, who knew so little of loving. And because she knew so much of love, her eyes filled to overflowing.

But presently she wiped the tears away and went back to the table. And she smiled at the Small Girl and at the Small Girl's father.

"And the potatoes were ivory," she said. "Oh, who would ask for turkey, when they can have a pie like this?"

The Gift of the Magi

By O. Henry

(Sydney William Porter)

ONE dollar and eighty-seven cents. That was all. And sixty cents of it was in pennies. Pennies saved one and two at a time by bulldozing the grocer and the vegetable man and the butcher until one's cheeks burned with the silent imputation of parsimony that such close dealing implied. Three times Della counted it. One dollar and eighty-seven cents. And the next day would be Christmas.

There was clearly nothing to do but flop down on the shabby little couch and howl. So Della did it. Which instigates the moral reflection that life is made up of sobs, sniffles, and smiles, with sniffles predominating.

While the mistress of the home is gradually subsiding from the first stage to the second, take a look at the home. A furnished flat at eight dollars per week. It did not exactly beggar description, but it certainly had that word on the lookout for the mendicancy squad.

In the vestibule below was a letter-box into which no letter would go, and an electric button from which no mortal finger could coax a ring. Also appertaining thereunto was a card bearing the name "Mr. James Dillingham Young."

The "Dillingham" had been flung to the breeze during a former period of prosperity when its possessor was being paid thirty dollars per week. Now, when the income was shrunk to twenty dollars, the letters of "Dillingham" looked blurred, as though they were thinking seriously of contracting to a modest and unassuming D. But whenever Mr. James Dillingham Young came home and reached his flat above he was called "Jim" and greatly hugged by Mrs. James Dillingham Young, already introduced to you as Della. Which is all very good.

Della finished her cry and attended to her cheeks with a powder-puff. She stood by the window and looked out dully at a gray cat walking a gray fence in a gray back yard. Tomorrow would be Christmas Day, and she had only $1.87 with which to buy Jim a present. She had been saving every penny she could for months, with this result. Twenty dollars a week doesn't go far. Expenses had been greater than she had calculated. They always are. Only $1.87 to buy a present for Jim. Her Jim. Many a happy hour she had spent planning for something nice for him. Something fine and rare and sterling—something just a little bit near to being worthy of the honor of being owned by Jim.

There was a pier-glass between the windows of the room. Perhaps you have seen a pier-glass in an eight-dollar flat. A very thin and very agile person may, by observing his reflection in a rapid sequence of longitudinal strips, obtain a fairly accurate conception of his looks. Della, being slender, had mastered the art.

Suddenly she whirled from the window and stood before the glass. Her eyes were shining brilliantly, but her face had lost its color within twenty seconds. Rapidly she pulled down her hair and let it fall to its full length.

Now, there were two possessions of the James Dillingham Youngs in which they both took a mighty pride. One was Jim's gold watch that had been his father's and his grandfather's. The other was Della's hair. Had the Queen of Sheba lived in the flat across the airshaft, Della would have let her hair hang out the window some day to dry just to depreciate Her Majesty's jewels and gifts. Had King Solomon been the janitor, with all his treasures piled up in the basement, Jim would have pulled out his watch every time he passed, just to see him pluck at his beard from envy.

So now Della's beautiful hair fell about her, rippling and shining like a cascade of brown waters. She did it up again nervously and quickly. Once she faltered for a minute and stood still while a tear or two splashed on the worn red carpet.

On went her old brown jacket; on went her old brown hat. With a whirl of skirts and with the brilliant sparkle still in her eyes, she fluttered out the door and down the stairs to the street.

Where she stopped the sign read: "Mme. Sofronie. Hair Goods of All Kinds." One flight up Della ran, and collected herself, panting. Madame, large, too white, chilly, hardly looked the "Sofronie."

"Will you buy my hair?" asked Della

"I buy hair," said Madame. "Take yer hat off and let's have a sight at the looks of it."

Down rippled the brown cascade.

"Twenty dollars," said Madame, lifting the mass with a practiced hand.

"Give it to me quick," said Della.

Oh, and the next two hours tripped by on rosy wings. Forget the hashed metaphor. She was ransacking the stores for Jim's present.

She found it at last. It surely had been made for Jim and no one else. There was no other like it in any of the stores, and she had turned all of them inside out. It was a platinum watch-chain, simple and chaste in design, properly proclaiming its value by substance alone and not by meretricious ornamentation—as all good things should do. It was even worthy of The Watch. As soon as she saw it she knew that it must be Jim's. It was like him. Quietness and value—the description applied to both. Twenty-one dollars they took from her for it, and she hurried home with the eighty-seven cents. With that chain on his watch Jim might be properly anxious about the time in any company. Grand as the watch was, he sometimes looked at it on the sly on account of the old leather strap that he used in place of a chain.

When Della reached home her intoxication gave way a little to prudence and reason. She got out her curling-irons and lighted the gas and went to work repairing the ravages made by generosity added to love. Which is always a tremendous task, dear friends—a mammoth task.

Within forty minutes her head was covered with tiny close-lying curls that made her look wonderfully like a truant schoolboy. She looked at her reflection in the mirror long, carefully, and critically.

"If Jim doesn't kill me," she said to herself, "before he takes a second look at me, he'll say I look like a Coney Island chorus girl. But what could I do—oh! what could I do with a dollar and eighty-seven cents?"

At seven o'clock the coffee was made and the frying-pan was on the back of the stove, hot and ready to cook the chops.

Jim was never late. Della doubled the watch chain in her hand and sat on the corner of the table near the door that he always entered. Then she heard his step on the stair away down on the first flight, and she turned white for just a moment. She had a habit of saying little silent prayers about the simplest everyday things, and now she whispered: "Please, God, make him think I am still pretty."

The door opened and Jim stepped in and closed it. He looked thin and very serious. Poor fellow, he was only twenty-two—and to be burdened with a family! He needed a new overcoat and he was without gloves.

Jim stepped inside the door, as immovable as a setter at the scent of quail. His eyes were fixed upon Della, and there was an expression in them that she could not read, and it terrified her. It was not anger, nor surprise, nor disapproval, nor horror, nor any of the sentiments that she had been prepared for. He simply stared at her fixedly with that peculiar expression on his face.

Della wriggled off the table and went for him.

"Jim, darling," she cried, "don't look at me that way. I had my hair cut off and sold it because I couldn't have lived through Christmas without giving you a present. It'll grow out again—you won't mind, will you? I just had to do it. My hair grows awfully fast. Say 'Merry Christmas!' Jim, and let's be happy. You don't know what a nice—what a beautiful, nice gift I've got for you."

"You've cut off your hair?" asked Jim, laboriously, as if he had not arrived at that patent fact yet even after the hardest mental labor.

"Cut it off and sold it," said Della. "Don't you like me just as well, anyhow? I'm me without my hair, ain't I?"

Jim looked about the room curiously.

"You say your hair is gone?" he said, with an air almost of idiocy.

"You needn't look for it," said Della. "It's sold, I tell you—sold and gone, too. It's Christmas Eve, boy. Be good to me, for it went for you. Maybe the hairs of my head were numbered," she went on with a sudden serious sweetness, "but nobody could ever count my love for you. Shall I put the chops on, Jim?"

Out of his trance Jim seemed to quickly wake. He enfolded his Della. For ten seconds let us regard with discreet scrutiny some inconsequential object in the other direction. Eight dollars a week or a million a year—what is the difference? A mathematician or a wit would give you the wrong answer. The Magi brought valuable gifts, but that was not among them. This dark assertion will be illuminated later on.

Jim drew a package from his overcoat pocket and threw it upon the table.

"Don't make any mistake, Dell," he said, "about me. I don't think there's anything in the way of a haircut or a shave or a shampoo that could make me like my girl any less. But if you'll unwrap that package you may see why you had me going awhile at first."

White fingers and nimble tore at the string and paper. And then an ecstatic scream of joy; and then, alas! a quick feminine change to hysterical tears and wails, necessitating the immediate employment of all the comforting powers of the lord of the flat.

For there lay The Combs—the set of combs that Della had worshiped for long in a Broadway window. Beautiful combs, pure tortoise shell, with jeweled rims—just the shade to wear in the beautiful vanished hair. They were expensive combs, she knew, and her heart had simply craved and yearned over them without the least hope of possession. And now they were hers, but the tresses that should have adorned the coveted adornments were gone.

But she hugged them to her bosom, and at length she was able to look up with dim eyes and a smile and say: "My hair grows so fast, Jim!"

And then Della leaped up like a little singed cat and cried, "Oh, oh!"

Jim had not yet seen his beautiful present. She held it out to him eagerly upon her open palm. The dull precious metal seemed to flash with a reflection of her bright and ardent spirit.

"Isn't it a dandy, Jim? I hunted all over town to find it. You'll have to look at the time a hundred times a day now. Give me your watch. I want to see how it looks on it."

Instead of obeying, Jim tumbled down on the couch and put his hands under the back of his head and smiled.

"Dell," said he, "let's put our Christmas presents away and keep 'em awhile. They're too nice to use just at present. I sold the watch to get the money to buy your combs. And now suppose you put the chops on."

The Magi, as you know, were wise men—wonderfully wise men—who brought gifts to the Babe in the manger. They invented the art of giving Christmas presents. Being wise, their gifts were no doubt wise ones, possibly bearing the privilege of exchange in case of duplication. And here I have lamely related to you the uneventful chronicle of two foolish children in a flat who most unwisely sacrificed for each other the greatest treasures of their house. But in a last word to the wise of these days let it be said that of all who give gifts these two were the wisest. Of all who give and receive gifts, such as they are wisest. Everywhere they are wisest. They are the Magi.

The Three Low Masses

How the Good Abbé Balaguère Was Led Headlong into Temptation by Visions of the Groaning Board

By Alphonse Daudet

"TWO turkeys stuffed with truffles, Garrigou?"

"Yes, Reverend Father, two magnificent turkeys crammed with truffles. I know a bit about it, for it was I who helped to stuff them. You would have said that their skins were going to burst in the roasting, they were stretched so tight."

"*Jésus-Maria!* And I who love truffles so! Give me my surplice quick, Garrigou. And besides the turkeys, what else did you see in the kitchen?"

"Oh, all sorts of good things. Since noon we have done nothing but pluck pheasants, pullets, grouse, and woodcocks. Feathers were flying all over. Then from the pond they brought eels and gold carp and trout and . . ."

"The trout are how big, Garrigou?"

"As big as this, Reverend Father. . . . Enormous."

"Ah, *mon Dieu!* I seem to see them. . . . Have you put wine in the cruets for the Mass?"

"Yes, Reverend Father, I have put wine in the carafes. But dear Lord! It isn't as good as what you are going to drink before long when you leave the Midnight Mass! If you had seen the dining-hall of the castle, all those shining bottles full of wine of all colours . . . and the silver plate, the engraved centrepiece, the flowers, the candelabra! Never have we seen such a *réveillon.* The Marquis has invited all the lords of the country round. There will be at least forty of you at table, not counting the bailiff and the notary. Ah, you're lucky to be among them, Reverend Father! Just to have smelt those beautiful turkeys, the odour of truffles follows me all around. . . . Mmmmmm!"

"Come, come, my child. Let us avoid the sin of gluttony, especially on Christmas Eve. Run along quickly and light the candles and ring the first bell for the Mass, for it's nearly midnight and we mustn't be late."

This conversation went on one Christmas Eve in the Year of Grace Sixteen-hundred-and-something, between the Reverend Dom Balaguère, former prior of the Barnabites, at this time chaplain to the lords of Trinquelage, and his little vestry-boy Garrigou, or at least what he thought was the little vestry-boy Garrigou, for you will learn that the devil that evening had taken the round face and the unformed features of the young sacristan the better to lead the Reverend Father into temptation and make him commit the frightful sin of gluttony. So, while the so-called Garrigou (ahem, ahem) rang the bells of the castle chapel with all his might, the Reverend Father finished putting on his robes in the little vestry; and, his mind already troubled by all these descriptions of good things to eat, he repeated to himself as he dressed:

"Roast turkeys. . . . Gold carp. . . . Trout as big as this!"

Outside, the night wind blew in competition with the music of the bells, and one by one lights appeared against the flank of Mont Ventoux, on whose summit stood the old towers of Trinquelage. It was the families of freemen who were coming to the Midnight Mass at the castle. They climbed the hill in groups of five or six, the father in front with a lantern in his hand, the women wrapped in their great brown mantles under which the children huddled for shelter. In spite of the lateness and the cold, all these good people were walking slowly, upheld by the idea that after the Mass was over there would be, as every year, a table set for them downstairs in the kitchens. From time to time, during the stiff climb, the carriage of some lord, preceded by torchbearers, twinkled its windows in the moonlight; or perhaps a mule trotted by, jingling its bells, and, by the light of the lanterns through the haze, the freemen recognized their bailiff and saluted him as he passed.

"Good evening, Master Arnoton!"

"Good evening, good evening, my children!"

The night was clear, the stars were bright in the cold. The breeze nipped a little, and a very fine snow, that slipped from clothing without wetting it, faithfully kept the tradition of a white

Christmas. On the very top of the hill the castle appeared as their goal, with its enormous bulk of towers, its gables, the belfry of the chapel rising into the blue-black sky, and a mass of little lights which winked and came and went, moving behind all the windows, and looking, against the sombre background of the building, like the sparks which run through the ashes of burnt paper. Once past the drawbridge and the postern, it was necessary to cross the first court, full of carriages, valets, and sedan-chairs, and all bright with the flames of the torches and the light from the kitchens. One heard the crackle from the turning spits, the clatter of casseroles, the sound of glass and silver being made ready for the feast. On top of that, a warm vapor, which smelt of roasted meat and strong seasoning and complicated sauces, made the freemen say, as it had made the chaplain and the bailiff and everybody else say:

"Lord! What a *réveillon* we are going to have after the Mass!"

Ding-ding-dong! Ding-ding-dong!

The first Mass is beginning. In the castle chapel, a miniature cathedral with interlocking arches and oak woodwork reaching to the tops of the walls, the tapestries had been hung, the candles lighted. And what a crowd! What fine clothes! First there is the Lord of Trinquelage in a suit of salmon taffeta, seated in the sculptured pews which surround the choir, and near him all the noble lords who are his guests. Opposite, in the *prie-Dieu* upholstered in velvet, the old dowager Marquise in her gown of flame-coloured brocade, and the young mistress of Trinquelage, wearing a high headdress of pleated lace in the latest style of the court of France, took their places. Farther back, dressed in black with great pointed perruques and shaven faces, could be seen the bailiff, Thomas Arnoton, and the notary, Master Ambroy, two grave notes among the transparent silks and the figured damasks. Then come the fat major-domos, the pages, the pikemen, the superintendents, and Dame Barbe, all her keys hanging at her side on a key-ring of fine silver. In the back, on benches, there are the lesser folk, the servants, the freemen and their families, and finally, down there by the door, which they open and shut discreetly, are the potboys who come in between two sauces to get a little whiff of the Mass and to bring an odour of *réveillon* into the gay chapel all warm with so many lighted candles.

Is it the sight of those little white caps which distracts the good Father? Isn't it rather Garrigou's bell, that mad little bell which tinkles at the foot of the altar in an infernal hurry and seems all the time to be saying:

"Hurry! Hurry! The sooner we are finished, the sooner we eat!"

The fact is that each time it tinkles, this devil's bell, the chaplain forgets his Mass and thinks only of the *réveillon*. He imagines the cooks in their excitement, the ovens where a regular forge-fire burns, the steam which rises from the half-tilted pot-lids, and in this steam he sees two magnificent turkeys, crammed, tight-stretched, stiff with truffles. Or perhaps he sees lines of pages passing, carrying dishes beclouded in tempting vapours, and with them he enters the great hall already prepared for the feast. Oh, glory! There's the immense table all loaded and glittering, the peacocks dressed up in their feathers, the pheasants with their reddish-brown wings, the ruby-coloured carafes, the pyramids of fruit shining out from among green leaves, and those marvellous fish of which Garrigou spoke (Oh, certainly, it *was* Garrigou) laid out on a bed of ferns, their scales like mother-of-pearl just as they came from the water, with a sprig of sweet-smelling grass in their monstrous mouths. The vision of these marvels was so lifelike that it seemed to Dom Balaguère all these fabulous dishes were served before him on the embroidery of the altar cloth, and two or three times, instead of saying *Dominus vobiscum* he caught himself saying grace. But aside from these slight wanderings, the worthy man filled his office most conscientiously, without skipping a line, without omitting a single genuflection; and everything moved well enough until the end of the first Mass. For you know that on Christmas Eve the same priest must celebrate three consecutive Masses.

"There's one of them!" the chaplain said to himself with a sigh of relief. Then, without losing an instant, he signalled his vestry-boy, or him whom he believed to be his vestry-boy, and . . .

"Ding-ding-dong! Ding-ding-dong!"

The second Mass is beginning, and with it also begins the sin of Dom Balaguère.

"Quick! Quick! Hurry!" cries Garrigou's little bell in its thin voice, and this time the unfortunate Dom Balaguère, abandoned to the demon of gluttony, dashes through the missal and devours its pages with the avidity of his over-sharpened appetite. Frantically he kneels, rises, goes through the motions of the Sign of the Cross, shortening all the gestures in order to be through more quickly. He scarcely stretches his arms toward the Scriptures, or strikes his chest at the *Confiteor*. It is a race between him and his vestry-boy to see who can jabber the more quickly. Readings and responses trip over each other, bump one another. Words half pronounced, without opening the mouth, for that would take too much time, and in incomprehensible murmurs.

"*Oremus* . . . ps . . . ps . . ."

"*Mea culpa* . . . pa . . . pa . . ."

Like wine-makers pressing the grapes in the tub in a great hurry, both of them stamp about in the Latin of the Mass, splashing it to all sides.

"*Dom* . . . *scum,*" says Dom Balaguère.

". . . *stutuo*," answers Garrigou. And all the time the devilish little bell is tinkling in their ears, like the bells they put on post-horses to make them gallop faster. You can imagine that at this rate a Mass is quickly out of the way.

"That's two of them!" says the chaplain, completely winded. Then, without taking time to breathe, red, perspiring, he comes down the steps of the altar and . . .

"Ding-ding-dong! Ding-ding-dong!"

The third Mass is beginning. Only a few steps more to reach the banquet-hall, but alas! as the *revéillon* comes nearer, the unfortunate Balaguère is gripped by the mad impatience of gluttony. The vision grows clearer. The golden carp, the roast turkeys are there, right there. . . . He touches them . . . he . . . Oh! Dear God! The dishes are smoking, the wines are breathing their aroma, and, shaking its maddened tongue, the little bell cries out to him:

"Quick! Quick! Still quicker!"

But how can he go any faster? His lips are scarcely moving. He is no longer pronouncing the words. He is all but cheating God entirely and filching His Mass from Him. And that's exactly what he does do, at last, poor soul! From temptation to temptation, he begins by skipping a verse, then two. Then the Scripture-reading is too long; he doesn't finish it. He scarcely touches the psalms, passes before the *Credo* without entering, skips the *Preface*, waves from a distance to the Lord's Prayer, and by leaps and bounds precipitates himself into eternal damnation, always followed by the infamous little Garrigou (Get thee behind me, Satan), who abets him with marvellous understanding, lifts up his gown, turns the pages two at a time, knocks against the pulpit, upsets the wine cruets, and incessantly rings the little bell louder and louder, faster and faster.

You should see the astonished faces of the congregation! Obliged to follow this Mass of which they do not understand a word, by mimicking the good Father, some rise when others are kneeling, some kneel when others are standing; all the gestures of this singular ceremony get mixed with each other as the congregation strikes all the different attitudes at the same time. The Christmas Star, moving along the roads of the sky towards the little stable, pales with horror at the sight of the confusion.

"The abbé goes too fast. . . . You can't follow him," murmurs
the old dowager as she shakes her head wildly.

Master Arnoton, his great steel spectacles on his nose, looks in
his missal to see where the devil the place is. But at bottom, not
one of the congregation is in the least angry that the Mass is going
at such breakneck speed; and when Dom Balaguère, his face shining, turns towards the congregation and cries with all his might:
"*Ite, missa est,*" the whole chapel answers him in a single voice
with a joyous "*Deo Gratias,*" so compelling that one could believe
oneself already at table, drinking the first toast of the *réveillon.*

Five minutes afterwards, the crowd of lords were seating themselves in the great hall, the chaplain in their midst. The castle, lit
from top to bottom, rang with singing and shouts and laughter;
and the venerable Dom Balaguère planted his fork in the wing of
a ruffed grouse and drowned his remorse for his sin in an ocean
of wine of the Popes and good meat gravy.

And would you like to know what came of it all? The poor holy
man ate so much and drank so much that he died the same night
in terrible agony, without even having had time to repent. . . .
Then, in the morning, he arrived in heaven with the sounds of
the feast of the night before still ringing in his ears, and you can
imagine how he was received.

"Out of my sight, thou bad Christian," said the Sovereign
Judge, the Master of us all. "Thy sin is great enough to wipe out
a whole life of virtue. Ah, thou hast stolen from me a Christmas
Mass. Well, thou shalt pay me three hundred of them in its place,
and thou shalt not enter into Paradise until thou shalt have said
those three hundred Christmas Masses in thy own chapel in the
presence of all those who have sinned with thee and by thy fault."

And that is the true legend of Dom Balaguère, as they tell it in
the country of olives. Today the Castle of Trinquelage no longer
exists, but the chapel still stands on the summit of Mont Ventoux,
in a clump of green oaks. The wind swings its sagging doors,
grass grows on the doorsill; there are birds' nests in the corners
of the altar and in the embrasures of the high windows whose
stained glass has disappeared long ago. It appears, however, that
every year at Christmas time, a supernatural light wanders among
those ruins, and that the peasants as they go to Christmas Mass

and to the *réveillon* see this spectral chapel lit with invisible tapers burning in the open air, in spite of snow and wind. You may laugh at that if you wish, but a wine-grower of the neighbourhood named Garrigue, doubtless a descendant of Garrigou, assured me that one Christmas Eve, when he had had only a little too much to drink, he got lost in the mountains near Trinquelage, and this is what he saw. Until eleven o'clock, nothing. Everything was silent, extinct, lifeless. Suddenly, towards midnight, a bell rang from the top of the steeple, an old, old bell which sounded as though it were leagues away. Pretty soon, on the road which climbs the hill, Garrigue saw lights twinkling and vague shadows moving. Under the porch of the chapel, people were walking and talking.

"Good evening, Master Arnoton!"

"Good evening, good evening, my children!"

When everyone had entered, my wine-grower, who was a brave man, approached quietly and, looking through the broken door, saw a singular spectacle. All those people he had watched as they passed were standing around the choir and in the ruined nave, as though the old benches still were there. Beautiful ladies in brocade with lace headdresses, lords in embroidery from head to foot, peasants in flowered jackets like our grandfathers used to wear, all looking old, faded, dusty, tired. From time to time the night birds, habitual lodgers in the chapel and awakened by all those lights, came and flew about the tapers, whose flame rose straight and hazy as though they were burning behind a gauze curtain. What amused Garrigue very much was a certain personage with great steel spectacles, who shook his black perruque every two minutes as one of those birds settled on it and flapped its wings silently.

In the back, a little old man of a child's stature, on his knees in the middle of the choir, shook a small tongueless, voiceless bell desperately, while a priest, dressed in cloth of gold, came and went before the altar reciting services of which you could hear not a word. Certainly that was Dom Balaguère, in the middle of his third Christmas Mass.

How Santa Claus Came to Simpson's Bar

By Bret Harte

IT HAD been raining in the valley of the Sacramento. The North Fork had overflowed its banks, and Rattlesnake Creek was impassable. The few boulders that had marked the summer ford at Simpson's Crossing were obliterated by a vast sheet of water stretching to the foothills. The up stage was stopped at Grangers; the last mail had been abandoned in the *tules*, the rider swimming for his life.

Nor was the weather any better in the foothills. The mud lay deep on the mountain road; the way to Simpson's Bar was indicated by broken-down teams and hard swearing. And farther on, cut off and inaccessible, rained upon and bedraggled, smitten by high winds and threatened by high water, Simpson's Bar, on the eve of Christmas day, 1862, clung like a swallow's nest to the rocky entablature and splintered capitals of Table Mountain, and shook in the blast.

As night shut down on the settlement, a few lights gleamed through the mist from the windows of cabins on either side of the highway. Happily most of the population were gathered at Thompson's store, clustered around a red-hot stove, at which they silently spat in some accepted sense of social communion that perhaps rendered conversation unnecessary.

Even the sudden splashing of hoofs before the door did not arouse them. Dick Bullen alone paused in the act of scraping out his pipe, and lifted his head, but no other one of the group indicated any interest in, or recognition of, the man who entered.

It was a figure familiar enough to the company, and known in Simpson's Bar as "The Old Man." A man of perhaps fifty years; grizzled and scant of hair, but still fresh and youthful of complexion. A face full of ready, but not very powerful sympathy, with a chameleon-like aptitude for taking on the shade and color of contiguous moods and feelings. He had evidently just left some hilarious companions, and did not at first notice the gravity of the group, but clapped the shoulder of the nearest man jocularly, and threw himself into a vacant chair.

"Jest heard the best thing out, boys! Ye know Smiley, over yar —Jim Smiley—funniest man in the Bar? Well, Jim was jest telling the richest yarn about ——"

"Smiley's a —— fool," interrupted a gloomy voice.

"A particular —— skunk," added another in sepulchral accents.

A silence followed these positive statements. The Old Man glanced quickly around the group. Then his face slowly changed. "That's so," he said, reflectively, after a pause, "certingly a sort of a skunk and suthin' of a fool. In course." He was silent for a moment as in painful contemplation of the unsavoriness and folly of the unpopular Smiley. "Dismal weather, ain't it?" he added, now fully embarked on the current of prevailing sentiment. "Mighty rough papers on the boys, and no show for money this season. And tomorrow's Christmas."

There was a movement among the men at this announcement, but whether of satisfaction or disgust was not plain. "Yes," continued the Old Man in the lugubrious tone he had, within the last few moments, unconsciously adopted—"yes, Christmas, and to-night's Christmas Eve. Ye see, boys, I kinder thought—that is, I sorter had an idee, jest passin' like, you know—that maybe ye'd all like to come over to my house tonight and have a sort of tear 'round. But I suppose, now, you wouldn't? Don't feel like it, maybe?" he added with anxious sympathy, peering into the faces of his companions.

"Well, I don't know," responded Tom Flynn with some cheerfulness. "P'r'aps we may. But how about your wife, Old Man? What does *she* say to it?"

The Old Man hesitated. His conjugal experience had not been a happy one, and the fact was known to Simpson's Bar. His first wife, a delicate, pretty little woman, had suffered keenly and secretly from the jealous suspicions of her husband, until one day he invited the whole Bar to his house to expose her infidelity. On arriving, the party found the shy, petite creature quietly engaged in her household duties, and retired abashed and discomfited. But the sensitive woman did not easily recover from the shock of this extraordinary outrage. It was with difficulty she regained her equanimity sufficiently to release her lover from the closet in which he was concealed and escape with him. She left a boy of three years to comfort her bereaved husband. The Old Man's present wife had been his cook. She was large, loyal, and aggressive.

Before he could reply, Joe Dimmick suggested with great directness that it was the "Old Man's house," and that, invoking the Divine Power, if the case were his own, he would invite whom he pleased, even if in so doing he imperiled his salvation. The Powers of Evil, he further remarked, should contend against him vainly. All this delivered with a terseness and vigor lost in this necessary translation.

"In course. Certainly. Thet's it," said the Old Man with a sympathetic frown. "Thar's no trouble about *thet*. It's my own house, built every stick on it myself. Don't you be afeard o' her, boys. She *may* cut up a trifle rough—ez wimmin do—but she'll come 'round." Secretly the Old Man trusted to the exaltation of liquor and the power of courageous example to sustain him in such an emergency.

As yet, Dick Bullen, the oracle and leader of Simpson's Bar, had not spoken. He now took his pipe from his lips. "Old Man, how's that yer Johnny gettin' on? Seems to me he didn't look so peart last time I seed him on the bluff heavin' rocks at Chinamen. Didn't seem to take much interest in it. Thar was a gang of 'em by yar yesterday—drownded out up the river—and I kinder thought o' Johnny, and how he'd miss 'em! Maybe, now, we'd be in the way ef he wus sick?"

The father, evidently touched not only by this pathetic picture of Johnny's deprivation, but by the considerate delicacy of the speaker, hastened to assure him that Johnny was better and that a "little fun might 'liven him up." Whereupon Dick arose, shook himself, and saying, "I'm ready. Lead the way, Old Man: here goes," himself led the way with a leap, a characteristic howl, and darted out into the night. As he passed through the outer room he caught up a blazing brand from the hearth. The action was repeated by the rest of the party, closely following and elbowing each other, and before the astonished proprietor of Thompson's grocery was aware of the intention of his guests, the room was deserted.

The night was pitchy dark. In the first gust of wind their temporary torches were extinguished, and only the red brands dancing and flitting in the gloom like drunken will-o'-the-wisps indicated their whereabouts. Their way led up Pine-Tree Cañon, at the head of which a broad, low, bark-thatched cabin burrowed in the mountain-side. It was the home of the Old Man, and the entrance to the tunnel in which he worked when he worked at all. Here the

crowd paused for a moment, out of delicate deference to their host, who came up panting in the rear.

"P'r'aps ye'd better hold on a second out yer, whilst I go in and see thet things is all right," said the Old Man, with an indifference he was far from feeling. The suggestion was graciously accepted, the door opened and closed on the host, and the crowd, leaning their backs against the wall and cowering under the eaves, waited and listened.

For a few moments there was no sound but the dripping of water from the eaves, and the stir and rustle of wrestling boughs above them. Then the men became uneasy, and whispered suggestion and suspicion passed from the one to the other. "Reckon she's caved in his head the first lick!" "Decoyed him inter the tunnel

and barred him up, likely." "Got him down and sittin' on him."
"Prob'ly b'ilin' suthin' to heave on us: stand clear the door, boys!"
For just then the latch clicked, the door slowly opened, and a voice
said, "Come in out o' the wet."

The voice was neither that of the Old Man nor of his wife. It
was the voice of a small boy, its weak treble broken by that preter-
natural hoarseness which only vagabondage and the habit of pre-
mature self-assertion can give. It was the face of a small boy that
looked up at theirs—a face that might have been pretty and even
refined but that it was darkened by evil knowledge from within,
and dirt and hard experience from without. He had a blanket
around his shoulders and had evidently just risen from his bed.
"Come in," he repeated, "and don't make no noise. The Old Man's
in there talking to mar," he continued, pointing to an adjacent
room which seemed to be a kitchen, from which the Old Man's
voice came in deprecating accents. "Let me be," he added, queru-
lously, to Dick Bullen, who had caught him up, blanket and all,
and was affecting to toss him into the fire, "let go o' me, you
d——d old fool, d'ye hear?"

Thus adjured, Dick Bullen lowered Johnny to the ground with
a smothered laugh, while the men, entering quietly, ranged themselves around a long table of rough boards which occupied the
center of the room. Johnny then gravely proceeded to a cupboard
and brought out several articles which he deposited on the table.
"Thar's whisky. And crackers. And red herons. And cheese." He
took a bite of the latter on his way to the table. "And sugar." He
scooped up a mouthful en route with a small and very dirty hand.
"And terbacker. Thar's dried appils too on the shelf, but I don't
admire 'em. Appils is swellin'. Thar," he concluded, "now wade
in, and don't be afeard. *I* don't mind the old woman. She don't
b'long to *me*. S'long."

He had stepped to the threshold of a small room, scarcely larger
than a closet, partitioned off from the main apartment, and holding in its dim recess a small bed. He stood there a moment looking
at the company, his bare feet peeping from the blanket, and
nodded.

"Hello, Johnny! You ain't goin' to turn in ag'in, are ye?" said
Dick.

"Yes, I are," responded Johnny, decidedly.

"Why, wot's up, old fellow?"

"I'm sick."

"How sick?"

"I've got a fevier. And childblains. And roomatiz," returned Johnny, and vanished within. After a moment's pause, he added in the dark, apparently from under the bedclothes, "And biles!" There was an embarrassing silence. The men looked at each other, and at the fire. Even with the appetizing banquet before them, it seemed as if they might again fall into the despondency of Thompson's grocery, when the voice of the Old Man, incautiously lifted, came deprecatingly from the kitchen.

"Certainly! Thet's so. In course they is. A gang o' lazy drunken loafers, and that ar Dick Bullen's the ornariest of all. Didn't hev no more *sabe* than to come round yar with sickness in the house and no provision. Thet's what I said: 'Bullen,' sez I, 'it's crazy drunk you are, or a fool,' sez I, 'to think o' such a thing.' 'Staples,' I sez, 'be you a man, Staples, and 'spect to raise h-ll under my roof and invalids lyin' round?' But they would come—they would. Thet's wot you must 'spect o' such trash as lays round the Bar."

A burst of laughter from the men followed this unfortunate exposure. Whether it was overheard in the kitchen, or whether the Old Man's irate companion had just then exhausted all other modes of expressing her contemptuous indignation, I cannot say, but a back door was suddenly slammed with great violence. A moment later and the Old Man reappeared, haply unconscious of the cause of the late hilarious outburst, and smiled blandly.

"The old woman thought she'd jest run over to Mrs. McFadden's for a sociable call," he explained, with jaunty indifference, as he took a seat at the board.

Oddly enough, it needed this untoward incident to relieve the embarrassment that was beginning to be felt by the party, and their natural audacity returned with their host. I do not propose to record the convivialities of that evening. The inquisitive reader will accept the statement that the conversation was characterized by the same intellectual exaltation, the same cautious reverence, the same fastidious delicacy, the same rhetorical precision, and the same logical and coherent discourse somewhat later in the evening, which distinguish similar gatherings of the masculine sex in more civilized localities and under more favorable auspices. No glasses were broken in the absence of any; no liquor was uselessly spilled on floor or table in the scarcity of that article.

It was nearly midnight when the festivities were interrupted. "Hush," said Dick Bullen, holding up his hand. It was the querulous voice of Johnny from his adjacent closet: "Oh, dad!"

The Old Man arose hurriedly and disappeared in the closet. Presently he reappeared. "His rheumatiz is coming on ag'in bad," he explained, "and he wants rubbin'." He lifted the demijohn of whisky from the table and shook it. It was empty. Dick Bullen put down his tin cup with an embarrassed laugh. So did the others. The Old Man examined their contents and said, hopefully, "I reckon that's enough; he don't need much. You hold on, all o' you, for a spell, and I'll be back"; and vanished in the closet with an old flannel shirt and the whisky. The door closed but imperfectly, and the following dialogue was distinctly audible:

"Now, sonny, whar does she ache worst?"

"Sometimes over yar and sometimes under yer; but it's most powerful from yer to yer. Rub yer, dad."

A silence seemed to indicate a brisk rubbing. Then Johnny:

"Hevin' a good time out yer, dad?"

"Yes, sonny."

"Tomorrer's Chrismiss; ain't it?"

"Yes, sonny. How does she feel now?"

"Better. Rub a little furder down. Wot's Chrismiss, anyway? Wot's it all about?"

"Oh, it's a day."

This exhaustive definition was apparently satisfactory, for there was a silent interval of rubbing. Presently Johnny again:

"Mar sez that everywhere else but yer everybody gives things to everybody Chrismiss, and then she jist waded inter you. She sez thar's a man they call Sandy Claws, not a white man, you know, but a kind o' Chinemin, comes down the chimbley night afore Chrismiss and gives things to chillern—boys like me. Puts 'em in their butes. Thet's what she tried to play upon me. Easy now, pop, whar are you rubbin' to; thet's a mile from the place. She jest made that up, didn't she, jest to aggrewate me and you? Don't rub thar. . . . Why, dad!"

In the great quiet that seemed to have fallen upon the house the sigh of the near pines and the drip of leaves without were very

distinct. Johnny's voice, too, was lowered as he went on: "Don't you take on now, fur I'm gettin' all right fast. Wot's the boys doin' out thar?"

The Old Man partly opened the door and peered through. His guests were sitting there sociably enough, and there were a few silver coins and a lean buckskin purse on the table. "Bettin' on suthin—some little game or 'nother. They're all right," he replied to Johnny, and recommenced his rubbing.

"I'd like to take a hand and win some money," said Johnny, reflectively, after a pause.

The Old Man glibly repeated what was evidently a familiar formula, that if Johnny would wait until he struck it rich in the tunnel he'd have lots of money, etc., etc.

"Yes," said Johnny, "but you don't. And whether you strike it or I win it, it's about the same. It's all luck. But it's mighty cur'o's about Chrismiss, ain't it? Why do they call it Chrismiss?"

Perhaps from some instinctive deference to the overhearing of his guests, or from some vague sense of incongruity, the Old Man's reply was so low as to be inaudible beyond the room.

"Yes," said Johnny, with some slight abatement of interest, "I've heard o' *him* before. Thar, that 'll do, dad. I don't ache near so bad as I did. Now wrap me tight in this yer blanket. So. Now," he added in a muffled whisper, "sit down yer by me till I go asleep." To assure himself of obedience, he disengaged one hand from the blanket and, grasping his father's sleeve, again composed himself to rest.

For some moments the Old Man waited patiently. Then the unwonted stillness of the house excited his curiosity, and without moving from the bed, he cautiously opened the door with his disengaged hand, and looked into the main room. To his infinite surprise it was dark and deserted. But even then a smoldering log on the hearth broke, and by the upspringing blaze he saw the figure of Dick Bullen sitting by the dying embers.

"Hello!"

Dick started, rose, and came somewhat unsteadily toward him.

"Whar's the boys?" said the Old Man.

"Gone up the cañon on a little *pasear*. They're coming back for me in a minit. I'm waitin' round for 'em. What are you starin' at,

Old Man?" he added, with a forced laugh. "Do you think I'm drunk?"

The Old Man might have been pardoned the supposition, for Dick's eyes were humid and his face flushed. He loitered and lounged back to the chimney, yawned, shook himself, buttoned up his coat, and laughed. "Liquor ain't so plenty as that, Old Man. Now don't you git up," he continued, as the Old Man made a movement to release his sleeve from Johnny's hand. "Don't you mind manners. Sit jest whar you be; I'm goin' in a jiffy. Thar, that's them now."

There was a low tap at the door. Dick Bullen opened it quickly, nodded "good night" to his host, and disappeared. The Old Man would have followed him but for the hand that still unconsciously grasped his sleeve. He could have easily disengaged it: it was small, weak, and emaciated. But perhaps because it *was* small, weak, and emaciated, he changed his mind, and, drawing his chair closer to the bed, rested his head upon it. The room flickered and faded before his eyes, reappeared, faded again, went out, and left him—asleep.

Meantime Dick Bullen, closing the door, confronted his companions.

"Are you ready?" said Staples.

"Ready," said Dick. "What's the time?"

"Past twelve," was the reply.

"Can you make it?—it's nigh on fifty miles, the round trip hither and yon."

"I reckon," returned Dick, shortly. "Whar's the mare?"

"Bill and Jack's holdin' her at the crossin'."

"Let 'em hold on a minit longer," said Dick.

He turned and re-entered the house softly. By the light of the guttering candle and dying fire he saw that the door of the little room was open. He stepped toward it on tiptoe and looked in. The Old Man had fallen back in his chair, snoring, his helpless feet thrust out in a line with his collapsed shoulders, and his hat pulled over his eyes. Beside him, on a narrow wooden bedstead, lay Johnny, muffled tightly in a blanket that hid all save a strip of forehead and a few curls damp with perspiration. Dick Bullen made a step forward, hesitated, and glanced over his shoulder into the deserted room. Everything was quiet. With a sudden resolution he parted his huge mustaches with both hands and stooped over the sleeping boy. But even as he did so a mischievous blast, lying in wait, swooped down the chimney, rekindled the hearth, and lit up the room with a shameless glow from which Dick fled in bashful terror.

His companions were already waiting for him at the crossing. Two of them were struggling in the darkness with some strange misshapen bulk, which, as Dick came nearer, took the semblance of a great yellow horse.

It was the mare. She was not a pretty picture. From her Roman nose to her rising haunches, from her arched spine hidden by the stiff *machillas* of a Mexican saddle, to her thick, straight, bony legs, there was not a line of equine grace. In her half-blind but wholly vicious white eyes, in her protruding under lip, in her monstrous color, there was nothing but ugliness and vice.

"Now then," said Staples, "stand cl'ar of her heels, boys, and up with you. Don't miss your first holt of her mane, and mind ye get your off stirrup *quick*. Ready!"

There was a leap, a scrambling struggle, a bound, a wild retreat of the crowd, a circle of flying hoofs, two springless leaps that jarred the earth, a rapid play and jingle of spurs, a plunge and then the voice of Dick somewhere in the darkness, "All right!"

A splash, a spark struck from the ledge in the road, a clatter in the rocky cut beyond, and Dick was gone.

Sing, O Muse, the ride of Richard Bullen! Sing, O Muse, of chivalrous men! the sacred quest, the doughty deeds, the battery of low churls, the fearsome ride and grewsome perils of the Flower of Simpson's Bar! Alack! she is dainty, this Muse! She will have none of this bucking brute and swaggering, ragged rider, and I must fain follow him in prose, afoot!

It was one o'clock, and yet he had only gained Rattlesnake Hill. For in that time Jovita had rehearsed to him all her imperfections and practiced all her vices. Thrice had she thrown up her Roman nose in a straight line with the reins, and, resisting bit and spur, struck out madly across country. Twice had she reared, and, rearing, fallen backward; and twice had the agile Dick, unharmed, regained his seat before she found her vicious legs again. And a mile beyond them, at the foot of a long hill, was Rattlesnake

Creek. Dick knew that here was the crucial test of his ability to perform his enterprise, set his teeth grimly, put his knees well into her flanks, and changed his defensive tactics to brisk aggression. Bullied and maddened, Jovita began the descent of the hill. Here the artful Richard pretended to hold her in with ostentatious objurgation and well-feigned cries of alarm. It is unnecessary to add that Jovita instantly ran away. Nor need I state the time made in the descent; it is written in the chronicles of Simpson's Bar. Enough that in another moment, as it seemed to Dick, she was splashing on the overflowed banks of Rattlesnake Creek. As Dick expected, the momentum she had acquired carried her beyond the point of balking, and, holding her well together for a mighty leap, they dashed into the middle of the swiftly flowing current. A few moments of kicking, wading, and swimming, and Dick drew a long breath on the opposite bank.

The road from Rattlesnake Creek to Red Mountain was tolerably level. Either the plunge in Rattlesnake Creek had dampened her baleful fire, or the art which led to it had shown her the superior wickedness of her rider, for Jovita no longer wasted her surplus energy in wanton conceits. Hollows, ditches, gravelly deposits, patches of freshly springing grasses, flew from beneath her rattling hoofs. She began to smell unpleasantly, once or twice she coughed slightly, but there was no abatement of her strength or speed. By two o'clock he had passed Red Mountain and begun the descent to the plain. At half past two Dick rose in his stirrups with a great shout. Stars were glittering through the rifted clouds, and beyond him, out of the plain, rose two spires, a flagstaff, and a straggling line of black objects. Dick jingled his spurs and swung his *riata*, Jovita bounded forward, and in another moment they swept into Tuttleville and drew up before the wooden piazza of "The Hotel of All Nations."

What transpired that night at Tuttleville is not strictly a part of this record. Briefly I may state, however, that after Jovita had been handed over to a sleepy ostler, whom she at once kicked into unpleasant consciousness, Dick sallied out with the barkeeper for a tour of the sleeping town. Lights still gleamed from a few saloons and gambling-houses; but, avoiding these, they stopped before several closed shops, and by persistent tapping and judicious outcry roused the proprietors from their beds, and made them unbar the doors of their magazines and expose their wares. Sometimes they were met by curses, but oftener by interest and some concern in their needs, and the interview was invariably concluded by a drink. It was three o'clock before this pleasantry was given over, and with a small waterproof bag of India-rubber strapped on his shoulders Dick returned to the hotel. But here he was waylaid by Beauty—Beauty opulent in charms, affluent in dress, persuasive in speech, and Spanish in accent! In vain she repeated the invitation in "Excelsior," happily scorned by all Alpine-climbing youth, and rejected by this child of the Sierras— a rejection softened in this instance by a laugh and his last gold coin. And then he sprang to the saddle and dashed down the lonely street and out into the lonelier plain, where presently the lights, the black line of houses, the spires, and the flagstaff sank into the earth behind him again and were lost in the distance.

The storm had cleared away, the air was brisk and cold, the outlines of adjacent landmarks were distinct, but it was half past four before Dick reached the meeting-house and the crossing of the county road. To avoid the rising grade he had taken a longer and more circuitous road, in whose viscid mud Jovita sank fetlock deep at every bound. It was a poor preparation for a steady ascent of five miles more; but Jovita, gathering her legs under her, took it with her usual blind, unreasoning fury, and a half-hour later reached the long level that led to Rattlesnake Creek. Another half-hour would bring him to the creek. He threw the reins lightly upon the neck of the mare, chirruped to her, and began to sing.

Suddenly Jovita shied with a bound that would have unseated a less practiced rider. Hanging to her rein was a figure that had leaped from the bank, and at the same time from the road before her arose a shadowy horse and rider. "Throw up your hands," commanded this second apparition, with an oath.

Dick felt the mare tremble, quiver, and apparently sink under him. He knew what it meant and was prepared.

"Stand aside, Jack Simpson. I know you, you d——d thief. Let me pass or ——"

He did not finish the sentence. Jovita rose straight in the air with a terrific bound, throwing the figure from her bit with a single shake of her vicious head, and charged with deadly malevolence down on the impediment before her. An oath, a pistol-shot, horse and highwayman rolled over in the road, and the next moment Jovita was a hundred yards away. But the good right arm of her rider, shattered by a bullet, dropped helplessly at his side. Without slacking his speed he shifted the reins to his left hand. But a few moments later he was obliged to halt and tighten the saddle-girths that had slipped in the onset. This in his crippled condition took some time. He had no fear of pursuit, but looking up he saw that the eastern stars were already paling, and that the distant peaks had lost their ghostly whiteness, and now stood out blackly against a lighter sky. Day was upon him. Then completely absorbed in a single idea, he forgot the pain of his wound, and mounting again dashed on toward Rattlesnake Creek. But now Jovita's breath came broken by gasps, Dick reeled in his saddle, and brighter and brighter grew the sky.

Ride, Richard; run, Jovita; linger, O day!

For the last few rods there was a roaring in his ears. Was it exhaustion from loss of blood, or what? He was dazed and giddy as he swept down the hill, and did not recognize his surroundings. Had he taken the wrong road, or was this Rattlesnake Creek?

It was. But the brawling creek he had swam a few hours before had risen, more than doubled its volume, and now rolled a swift and resistless river between him and Rattlesnake Hill. For the first time that night Richard's heart sank within him. The river, the mountain, the quickening east, swam before his eyes. He shut them to recover his self-control. In that brief interval, by some fantastic mental process, the little room at Simpson's Bar and the figures of the sleeping father and son rose upon him. He opened his eyes wildly, cast off his coat, pistol, boots, and saddle, bound his precious pack tightly to his shoulders, grasped the bare flanks of Jovita with his bared knees, and with a shout dashed into the yellow water. A cry rose from the opposite bank as the head of a man and horse struggled for a few moments against the battling current, and then were swept away amidst uprooted trees and whirling driftwood.

The Old Man started and woke. The fire on the hearth was dead, the candle in the outer room flickering in its socket, and somebody was rapping at the door. He opened it, but fell back with a cry before the dripping, half-naked figure that reeled against the doorpost.

"Dick?"

"Hush! Is he awake yet?"

"No,—but, Dick? ——"

"Dry up, you old fool! Get me some whisky *quick*!" The Old Man flew and returned with—an empty bottle! Dick would have sworn, but his strength was not equal to the occasion. He staggered, caught at the handle of the door, and motioned to the Old Man.

"Thar's suthin' in my pack yer for Johnny. Take it off. I can't."

The Old Man unstrapped the pack and laid it before the exhausted man.

"Open it, quick!"

He did so with trembling fingers. It contained only a few poor toys—cheap and barbaric enough, goodness knows, but bright with paint and tinsel. One of them was broken; another, I fear, was irretrievably ruined by water; and on the third—ah me! there was a cruel spot.

"It don't look like much, that's a fact," said Dick, ruefully, "but it's the best we could do. . . . Take 'em, Old Man, and put 'em in his stocking, and tell him—tell him, you know. . . . Hold me, Old Man—" The Old Man caught at his sinking figure. "Tell him"—said Dick, with a weak little laugh, "tell him Sandy Claus has come."

And even so, bedraggled, ragged, unshaven, and unshorn, with one arm hanging helplessly at his side, Santa Claus came to Simpson's Bar and fell fainting on the first threshold. The Christmas dawn came slowly after, touching the remoter peaks with the rosy warmth of ineffable love. And it looked so tenderly on Simpson's Bar that the whole mountain, as if caught in a generous action, blushed to the skies.

The Shepherd

A Footnote to the Christmas Story

By HEYWOOD BROUN

THE host of heaven and the angel of the Lord had filled the sky with radiance. Now the glory of God was gone and the shepherds and the sheep stood under dim starlight. The men were shaken by the wonders they had seen and heard and, like the animals, they huddled close.

"Let us now," said the eldest of the shepherds, "go unto Bethlehem, and see this thing which has come to pass, which the Lord hath made known unto us."

The City of David lay beyond a far, high hill, upon the crest of which there danced a star. The men made haste to be away, but as they broke out of the circle there was one called Amos who remained. He dug his crook into the turf and clung to it.

"Come," cried the eldest of the shepherds, but Amos shook his head. They marveled, and one called out: "It is true. It was an angel. You heard the tidings. A Saviour is born!"

"I heard," said Amos. "I will abide."

The eldest walked back from the road to a little knoll on which Amos stood.

"You do not understand," the old man told him. "We have a sign from God. An angel commanded us. We go to worship the Saviour, who is even now born in Bethlehem. God has made His will manifest."

"It is not in my heart," replied Amos.

And now the eldest of the shepherds was angry.

"With your own eyes," he cried out, "you have seen the host of heaven in these dark hills. And you heard, for it was like the thunder when 'Glory to God in the highest' came ringing to us out of the night."

And again Amos said, "It is not in my heart."

Another shepherd then broke in. "Because the hills still stand

and the sky has not fallen, it is not enough for Amos. He must have something louder than the voice of God."

Amos held more tightly to his crook and answered, "I have need of a whisper."

They laughed at him and said, "What should this voice say in your ear?"

He was silent and they pressed about him and shouted mockingly, "Tell us now. What says the God of Amos, the little shepherd of a hundred sheep?"

Meekness fell away from him. He took his hands from off the crook and raised them high.

"I too am a god," said Amos in a loud, strange voice, "and to my hundred sheep I am a saviour."

And when the din of the angry shepherds about him slackened, Amos pointed to his hundred.

"See my flock," he said. "See the fright of them. The fear of the bright angel and of the voices is still upon them. God is busy in Bethlehem. He has no time for a hundred sheep. They are my sheep. I will abide."

This the others did not take so much amiss, for they saw now that there was a terror in all the flocks and they too knew the ways of sheep. And before the shepherds departed on the road to Bethlehem toward the bright star, each talked to Amos and told him what he should do for the care of the several flocks. And yet one or two turned back a moment to taunt Amos, before they reached the dip in the road which led to the City of David. It was said, "We shall see new glories at the throne of God, and you, Amos, you will see sheep."

Amos paid no heed, for he thought to himself, "One shepherd the less will not matter at the throne of God." Nor did he have time to be troubled that he was not to see the Child who was come to save the world. There was much to be done among the flocks and Amos walked between the sheep and made under his tongue a clucking noise, which was a way he had, and to his hundred and to the others it was a sound more fine and friendly than the voice of the bright angel. Presently the animals ceased to tremble and they began to graze as the sun came up over the hill where the star had been. "For sheep," said Amos to himself, "the angels shine too much. A shepherd is better."

With the morning the others came up the road from Bethlehem, and they told Amos of the manger and of the wise men who had mingled there with shepherds. And they described to him the gifts: gold, frankincense, and myrrh. And when they were done they said, "And did you see wonders here in the fields with the sheep?"

Amos told them, "Now my hundred are one hundred and one," and he showed them a lamb which had been born just before the dawn.

"Was there for this a great voice out of heaven?" asked the eldest of the shepherds.

Amos shook his head and smiled, and there was upon his face that which seemed to the shepherds a wonder even in a night of wonders.

"To my heart," he said, "there came a whisper."

4

Words and Music for Christmas Carols Uncle Toby Knows the Family Will Enjoy: All of Them Old Familiar Friends from Childhood Days.

O Little Town of Bethlehem

PHILLIPS BROOKS

LEWIS H. REDNER, 1868

1. O lit-tle town of Beth-le-hem, How still we see thee lie!
2. For Christ is born of Ma - ry, And, ga-thered all a - bove,
3. How si-lent-ly, how si-lent-ly, The won-drous gift is giv'n!
4. O ho-ly Child of Beth-le-hem! De-scend to us, we pray;

A - bove thy deep and dream-less sleep The si - lent stars go by;
While mor-tals sleep, the an - gels keep Their watch of won-d'ring love.
So God im-parts to hu-man hearts The bless-ings of His heav'n.
Cast out our sin, and en - ter in, Be born in us to - day.

Yet in thy dark streets shin - eth The ev - er-last-ing Light;
O morn-ing stars, to - ge - ther Pro-claim the ho - ly birth!
No ear may hear His com - ing, But in this world of sin,
We hear the Christ-mas an - gels The great glad tid-ings tell;

The hopes and fears of all the years Are met in thee to - night.
And prais - es sing to God the King, And peace to men on earth.
Where meek souls will re-ceive Him still, The dear Christ en - ters in.
Oh, come to us, a - bide with us, Our Lord Em - ma - nu - el!

Silent Night! Holy Night!

FRANZ GRUBER, 1818

1. Si - lent night! Ho - ly night! All is calm,
2. Si - lent night! Ho - ly night! Shep - herds quake
3. Si - lent night! Ho - ly night! Son of God,

all is bright Round yon Vir - gin Mo - ther and Child!
at the sight, Glo - ries stream from hea - ven a - far,
love's pure light, Ra - diant beams from Thy ho - ly face,

Ho - ly In - fant, so ten - der and mild, Sleep in
Heav'n - ly hosts sing Al - le - lu - ia, Christ the
With the dawn of re - deem - ing grace Je - sus,

hea - ven - ly peace. Sleep in hea - ven - ly peace.
Sa - viour is born, Christ the Sa - viour is born.
Lord, at Thy birth, Je - sus, Lord, at Thy birth.

God Rest Ye Merry, Gentlemen

Traditional (SANDYS, 1833)

Mode I

M. M. ♩ = 120

1. God rest you mer-ry, Gen-tle-men, Let no-thing you dis-may,
2. In Beth-le-hem in Jew-ry This bless-ed babe was born,
3. From God our heav'n-ly Fa-ther A bless-ed an-gel came,

For Je-sus Christ our Sa-viour Was born up-on this day,
And laid with-in a man-ger, Up-on this bless-ed morn;
And un-to cer-tain shep-herds Brought tid-ings of the same,

To save us all from Sa-tan's power When we were gone a-stray:
The which His mo-ther Ma-ry No-thing did take in scorn:
How that in Beth-le-hem was born The Son of God by name:

CHORUS

O tid-ings of com-fort and joy, com-fort and

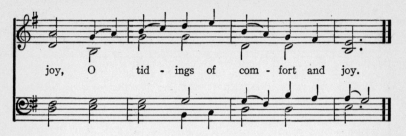

joy, O tid - ings of com - fort and joy.

4 'Fear not,' then said the angel,
　'Let nothing you affright,
This day is born a Saviour,
　Of virtue, power, and might;
So frequently to vanquish all
　The friends of Satan quite:'
　　　　　　　　　CHORUS

5 The shepherds at those tidings
　Rejoiced much in mind,
And left their flocks a-feeding,
　In tempest, storm and wind,
And went to Bethlehem straightway
　This Blessed Babe to find:
　　　　　　　　　CHORUS

6 But when to Bethlehem they came,
　Whereat this Infant lay,
They found Him in a manger,
　Where oxen feed on hay;
His Mother Mary kneeling,
　Unto the Lord did pray:
　　　　　　　　　CHORUS

7 Now to the Lord sing praises,
　All you within this place,
And with true love and brotherhood
　Each other now embrace;
This holy tide of Christmas
　All other doth deface:
　　　　　　　　　CHORUS

163

It Came Upon the Midnight Clear

WILLIS, 1850

1. It came up-on the mid-night clear, That glo-rious song of old,
2. Still through the clov - en skies they come, With peace-ful wings un-furl'd;
3. O ye, be-neath life's crush-ing load, Whose forms are bend-ing low,
4. For lo! the days are hast'-ning on, By pro-phets seen of old,

From an - gels, bend-ing near the earth, To touch their harps of gold:
And still their heav'n-ly mu - sic floats O'er all the wea - ry world;
Who toil a - long the climb-ing way With pain-ful steps and slow!
When with the ev - er cir-cling years, Shall come the time fore-told:

"Peace on the earth, good-will to men From heav'n's all gra-cious king."
A - bove its sad and low - ly plains They bend on hov'-ring wing.
Look now, for glad and gold-en hours Come swift-ly on the wing:
When the new heav'n and earth shall own The Prince of Peace their king,

The world in so-lemn still-ness lay To hear the an-gels sing.
And ev - er o'er its Ba-bel sounds The bless-ed an-gels sing.
O rest be - side the wea-ry road, And hear the an-gels sing.
And the whole world send back the song Which now the an-gels sing.

We Three Kings of Orient Are

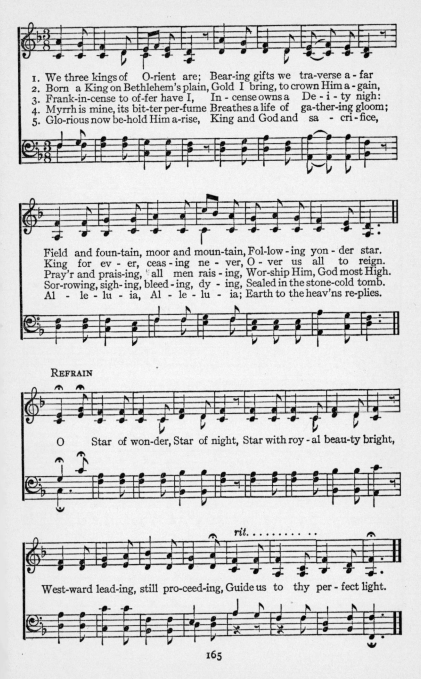

1. We three kings of O-rient are; Bear-ing gifts we tra-verse a-far
2. Born a King on Bethlehem's plain, Gold I bring, to crown Him a-gain,
3. Frank-in-cense to of-fer have I, In-cense owns a De-i-ty nigh:
4. Myrrh is mine, its bit-ter per-fume Breathes a life of ga-ther-ing gloom;
5. Glo-rious now be-hold Him a-rise, King and God and sa-cri-fice,

Field and foun-tain, moor and moun-tain, Fol-low-ing yon-der star.
King for ev-er, ceas-ing ne-ver, O-ver us all to reign.
Pray'r and prais-ing, all men rais-ing, Wor-ship Him, God most High.
Sor-row-ing, sigh-ing, bleed-ing, dy-ing, Sealed in the stone-cold tomb.
Al-le-lu-ia, Al-le-lu-ia; Earth to the heav'ns re-plies.

REFRAIN

O Star of won-der, Star of night, Star with roy-al beau-ty bright,

rit.

West-ward lead-ing, still pro-ceed-ing, Guide us to thy per-fect light.

O Come, All Ye Faithful

(*Adeste Fideles*)

1. O come, all ye faith - ful, joy - ful and tri - um - phant,
1. *A - de - ste fi - de - les, Lae - ti tri - um - phan - tes,*

O come ye, O come ye to Beth - le - hem;
Ve - ni - te, ve - ni - te in Beth - le - hem,

Come and be - hold Him, born the King of an - gels,
Na - tum vi - de - te, Re - gem an - ge - lo - rum,

REFRAIN

O come, let us a - dore Him, O come, let us a-
Ve - ni - te a - do - re - mus, Ve - ni - te a - do-

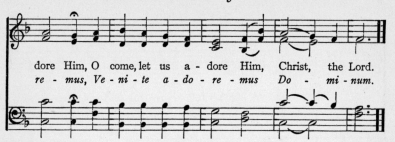

dore Him, O come, let us a - dore Him, Christ, the Lord.
re - mus, Ve - ni - te a - do - re - mus Do - mi - num.

2 Sing, choirs of angels, sing in exultation,
O sing, all ye citizens of heav'n above;
Glory to God, all glory in the highest.
Refrain: O come, let us adore Him, etc. . . .

3 Yea, Lord, we greet Thee, born this happy morning,
Jesus, to Thee be all glory giv'n;
Word of the Father, now in flesh appearing.
Refrain: O come, let us adore Him, etc. . . .

2 *Deum de Deo*
Lumen de lumine
Gestant puellae viscera;
Deum verum,
Genitum non factum;
Venite adoremus Dominum.

3 *Contet nunc "io",*
Chorus angelorum,
Contet nunc aula.
Caelestium,
Gloria in excelsis deo;
Venite adoremus Dominum.

4 *Ergo qui natus,*
Die hodierna,
Jesu, tibi sit gloria.
Patris aeterni,
Verbum caro factum;
Venite adoremus Dominum.

The First Noel

Mode 3 (in modern rhythm)

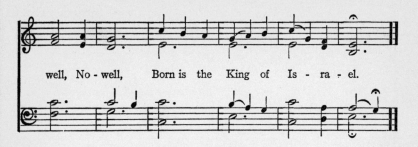

well, No - well, Born is the King of Is - ra - el.

3 And by the light of that same star,
   Three wise-men came from country far;
   To seek for a King was their intent,
   And to follow the star wherever it went.
Refrain: Nowell, Nowell, Nowell, Nowell,
   Born is the King of Israel.

4 This star drew nigh to the northwest,
   O'er Bethlehem it took its rest,
   And there it did both stop and stay,
   Right over the place where Jesus lay.
Refrain: Nowell, Nowell, Nowell, Nowell,
   Born is the King of Israel.

Good King Wenceslas

M.M. ♩= 104

(Chorus)
1. Good King Wen-ces-las look'd out On the Feast of Ste - phen,
(Tenor Solo)
2. "Hi-ther, page, and stand by me, If thou know'st it, tell - ing,
(Tenor Solo)
3. "Bring me flesh, and bring me wine, Bring me pine - logs hi - ther;

When the snow lay round a - bout, Deep and crisp and ev - en;
Yon - der pea-sant, who is he? Where and what his dwell - ing?"
Thou and I will see him dine When we bear them thi - ther."

Bright-ly shone the moon that night, Though the frost was cru - el,
(Treble Solo)
"Sire, he lives a good league hence, Un - der-neath the mount - ain;
(Chorus)
Page and mo-narch forth they went, Forth they went to - geth - er;

rit.

When a poor man came in sight, Gath'-ring win-ter fu - el.
Right a-gainst the fo'- rest fence, By Saint Ag-nes' foun - tain."
Through the rude wind's wild la-ment And the bit-ter wea - ther.

(*Treble Solo*)

4 "Sire, the night is darker now,
 And the wind blows stronger;
Fails my heart, I know not how,
 I can go no longer."

(*Tenor Solo*)

"Mark my footsteps, my good page,
 Tread thou in them boldly;
Thou shalt find the winter's rage
 Freeze thy blood less coldly."

(*Chorus*)

5 In his master's steps he trod,
 Where the snow lay dinted;
Heat was in the very sod
 Which the saint had printed;
Therefore, Christian men, be sure,
 Wealth or rank possessing,
Ye who now will bless the poor,
 Shall yourselves find blessing.

5

How to Plan an Old-Fashioned Christmas:
Uncle Toby's Suggestions for the Crèche, the
Tree, the Table; Games, Decorations, and Amuse-
ments of All Kinds, Tested Through the Years.

How to Plan an Old-Fashioned Christmas

WHEN Uncle Toby discusses plans for Christmas, he is always very firm about one thing. "Don't talk to me," he says, "about making Christmas simple this year. Simple indeed! What other holiday is meant to be so brimful of abundance and activity, of heaping up and pouring out, of bustling, furbishing, and doing up brown? Let no one ever feel that his holiday celebrations are going to be a burden or a bore. Make Christmas easy, to be sure, but simple—never!"

Preparations may well start in the lull after New Year's, when the fruit cake for the next year is made. Tempting but uncut, it is covered with sweet wine, sealed up in a brown earthenware jar, and stored away in a cool cellar or closet for almost twelve months. This is a double economy: a saving in time just before the next holiday, and a saving in cake. For delicious as it tastes, the wine-steeped pastry is so rich that even the hardiest of young eaters can manage only a couple of slices.

The Most Economical Fruit Cake;— and Candy That Keeps

The Christmas planning really begins, however, just after Thanksgiving. Since hard candies and candied fruit taste just as good as other sweets but keep better, they are made about December 1st and stored away. Fudge will keep soft if half an apple is packed away in the box. One grapefruit shell candied whole can be used as a container for the candied orange, lemon, and citron, and several grapefruit-baskets made at the same time may come in handy as last-minute gifts. About the 15th of December, Uncle Toby makes out a list of the things he feels he alone can do, and other lists to which he adds from time to time for everyone else in the house. These he tacks up in a convenient, inconspicuous place, and his helpers make a game of reporting progress at the

How to Turn Yule Tasks into Good Fun

174

tasks. There are minor failures, of course, but by the time Christmas Eve arrives, it would be hard to believe that some of the work hadn't been done by magic.

THE CRÈCHE

Uncle Toby has a tree, of course. But first about the crèche. One year he found himself in a Southern town where a fir tree couldn't be cut or bought, so that everyone set up in its place a miniature manger surrounded by tiny figures of the Holy Family, wise men, shepherds, and all sorts of animals. Some people get their crèche all ready-made in a shop, but more often they build it up at home from dolls and toy animals, or from cardboard cut-out figures. Ever since that Christmas, Uncle Toby has had a crèche as well as a tree. During the previous Christmas season he has clipped from papers and magazines every coloured Christmas picture, and his last year's Christmas cards he has piled away, together with the clippings, in a big box until some rainy day when the youngsters come begging for something new to play. Out come the box, paste, scissors, and cardboard, and before the year is half over, the children will have cut out and mounted on cardboard stands a whole new set of little figures for the crèche. If the Christmas cards are stiff enough, they need only an additional strip pasted on the back to make the cut-out figures stand up. Each year new figures are added, or substituted for less beautiful and durable ones left over from the last.

An Old, Old Ceremony for a New Kind of Crèche

After the crèche is all in place on the living-room table, several days before the tree is brought in, Uncle Toby makes a little ceremony of repeating the words of St. Francis, who more than seven hundred years ago built the first crèche. In the cave in the woods where he lived, St. Francis set up an altar with a manger beside it, saying: "I would make a memorial of that child who was born in Bethlehem, and in some sort behold with bodily eyes the hardship of his infant state." Then the children sing "Holy Night" (see page 161) and they all feel that Christmas has come at last.

THE TREE

Some people are considered dangerously old-fashioned because of their stand on the candle question. They like electric-light orna-

When to Have Two Trees, and How to Decorate One of Them, to Which Is Added a Note on the Candle Question

ments well enough and have some burning all through the holidays. But, they rightly maintain, nothing can take the place of real candles. If the tree is firmly set up—which it should be, anyway—and if the candles are placed with care in good solid holders, there is no earthly reason why you shouldn't enjoy at least once the lovely twinkling light that they alone can give. (Uncle Toby can't recall a single case in his own family of a Christmas tree catching fire in the pre-electric-light days; and as for the

present, statisticians seem to agree that far more Christmas fires occur from insufficient testing of electric circuits than from candles.) As for their being untidy—well, if you begin talking about that, you may as well eliminate Christmas.

The big tree should go in the living- or dining-room, loaded with all the traditional ornaments, from wax angels to popcorn strings. (Does anyone need to be told how to decorate the tree?) But if there are lots of young guests, it is good to put a smaller one in a playroom, and this does have rather special decorations. They should be either unbreakable or edible, so that the smallest reveller can't injure himself with them. Wooden or rubber balls coloured with hard, bright paint alternate with sugar cookies plain and iced, animal crackers, fruit and popcorn balls, all tied on with bits of thread. If the children know they can eat from their own tree, they are less likely to take liberties with more indigestible grown-up candies and cakes. Gifts, of course, are placed under the big tree to be opened Christmas Eve or morning, depending on the custom of the family.

WREATHS AND GARLANDS

Here are some of the things Uncle Toby does with his Christmas greens.

To the holly wreath that hangs on the front door he ties a little cluster of clear-toned sleigh-bells which give a merry jingle every time some one goes in or out. Once he put them on a wreath or two inside the house, but he warns you this is a little too much. The bells are part of a whole set he got at second hand from a harness dealer, and on page 179 you will find what good use he makes of the rest.

The Wreath of Holly Puts on Some New Trappings

Have you ever argued with yourself about the wreaths for the windows? Do you turn their show side in or out? One way to solve the problem is to hang half as many and make them double—two wreaths of the same size backed up against each other, so that Christmas can look both ways unashamed. If the holly has few berries on it, firm red cranberries can be strung on a length of picture wire and wound in and out among the leaves. Not too many to a wreath, however.

The cranberry string once gave Uncle Toby an idea when he was making up a basket for a poor family he knew. Why, he asked himself, should such attractive things as fresh vegetables all be done up in plain parcels? And so he made them into a wreath. While the children strung the berries—this time on clean white threads—he arranged a rather large wire hoop.

The More Lowly Greens Take on Dignity as Edible Garlands

Carrots and parsnips with long feathery tops tied along the hoop furnished most of the green, together with a bit of parsley and finucchi. A couple of red peppers and purple onions run through with string filled in. And then the cranberries were looped on—not wound in, because that would make them too hard to get off. The result was so gay and cheerful that Uncle Toby straightway made another wreath for his own kitchen, where it hung until December 26th and then mysteriously disappeared. (This is the time to mention that salad and a vegetable dinner are the rule at Uncle Toby's the day after Christmas, for too much feasting is as bad as too little.)

Festoons of laurel or ground pine, or both woven together, hang round the moulding in at least one room. They are easiest to arrange if they are made into one long piece and then caught up on S-shaped picture hangers with a bit of red ribbon every three or four feet. If you use ground pine, put it up rather later than the holly or laurel, for it is inclined to dry out quickly.

Hooks (and Ayes) for the Laurel and Pine

Boughs of pine or fir have a place on the mantel. They may be laid both ways from the middle, stumps together at the center, with a red ribbon or Cellophane bow tied round where they meet. Or small boughs may be piled along the whole length, with a bowl of holly and laurel arranged at one end to cover the bare stumps. Some of the brightest and best of the cut-out figures left over from the crèche stand forth gaily in front of the dark green, and one year in Uncle Toby's house a large silver star with tinsel rays was hung at the high end to guide the Three Wise Men and their caravan marching toward it all along the mantelshelf.

Fir Branches and a Spot of Color for the Mantelshelf

Breakfast on Christmas day is very plain—fruit cup and toast. But for the children, sober fare is decorated a bit. Half a banana stands upright in each fruit-dish, like a candle, with a Brazil nut stuck vertically in the top. Since the nut contains a good deal of oil, it can be lighted before the dish is brought in, forerunner of the pudding and echo of the tree.

Have Frills for the Children's Breakfast — But the King of Birds Demands a Table That Is Formal and Very Modest Indeed

The Christmas dinner-table is usually decorated with a low bowl of smilax and fruit in the centre, the long green vines stretching out across the cloth to four red candles in low holders placed as widely as the table permits, without making it difficult to serve. Nothing on the table should overshadow the turkey. A sprig of holly tucked into each napkin adds a bright touch, and there should be one fine sprig saved to top off the pudding. Plans for the Christmas dinner itself will be found on page 184.

GAMES

Magic Bells

After the dinner the games—first those that require little effort. Everyone is handed a sleigh-bell, tied with a piece of red string. Then while Uncle Toby, because he is the best player, leaves the room, his guests decide on a series of antics they want him to perform. He must, for instance, take a certain red ball from the tree and present it to the biggest boy; then pick up the littlest girl and take her under the mistletoe for a kiss. When this is agreed, Uncle Toby returns and is greeted with a faint jingling of bells. If he moves in the direction of the tree, the bells jingle louder and louder until he touches the certain ball. If he makes a wrong step, or touches any other ornament, the bells immediately grow fainter. And so on, through all the motions, he is guided by more or by less jingling. This looks very easy and one of the guests begs to go out while the company thinks up something really hard. But when he comes back and gets only a faint jingle no matter where he steps, he is puzzled. It may take him five minutes to figure out that he is expected to stand still and sing.

A Noisy Sport But Sedentary

Word Scramble

A very little jingling is enough, and by now most of the company is ready for something that takes thought if not action. Pencils and paper are passed round, and a prize is offered to the person who in the space of two minutes can make the most words by twisting around a selection of the letters contained in "Christmas." Proper names and two-letter words don't count. Thirty-five to forty words is a good average, and the prize is a square of Uncle Toby's famous fruit cake in a fancy box. The game can go on with such words as "fruit cake" or even "Uncle Toby," which may yield as many as sixty answers.

An Amusement for Those Who Like to Ponder

Stagecoach

Now for a bit of excitement—Stagecoach, of course. Everyone takes as his name some part of the coach or its contents:

Not Brains But Speed in Action Counts Here

wheel, window, springs, driver, whip, fussy lady traveller, and so on. Just one too few chairs are set out, and then Uncle Toby, for whom there is no chair, begins to tell a story which centres round a trip in a stagecoach. When he mentions "springs," the person assigned to be the *springs* must leap up and squeak. If he says, "The driver cracked his whip," *driver* rises with a "giddap" and *whip* goes "crack-crack." But when the story brings in the word "stagecoach," everyone must jump up and change place. In the shuffle Uncle Toby dives for a seat, and the person left over must continue the story.

A variant of the game, whereby someone is eliminated every time, may be worked this way: Uncle Toby is the permanent story-teller, but he scrambles for a chair at the general shift. The player who fails to find one is out, and the chair Uncle Toby captured is taken away. He himself may possibly not get a place, but he is given a handicap of three such failures. On the fourth he must retire ignominiously and give over the story to the last player to go out. A prize is won by the part of the coach that holds together longest.

Yawning for the Cheese

Now an interlude of quiet. Uncle Toby recalls, not without a shudder, that about two hundred years ago the English conceived an unnatural and mysterious boredom with Christmas, and in their perversity they invented a very good game called "Yawning for the Cheese." The guests are invited to loll back in their chairs and observe while each in turn yawns. As it goes round the circle, jaws begin involuntarily to drop. Finally the guest who by popular vote produces the most prodigious, natural, and infectious yawn gets the prize—a jar of Cheddar cheese in wine. Meantime the littlest girl has taken the game too seriously, is quite overcome by it all, and has to be carried off to bed.

A Really Scandalous Old English Game Is Here Turned Respectable

Two Old Favorites

Two more old English games have been played especially at Christmas time these six hundred years and more—Blind Man's

Buff and Hot Cockles. The first needs no explanation. The second is an amusing form of forfeits. **Old Scrooge's Niece Knew How to Play These Games** The player who is *It* kneels with his head against someone's knees. The others come up and give him a resounding spank, and if he guesses correctly who delivered the blow, the guilty one must pay a forfeit. There are other old English games, such as Rowland Bo and The Parson Has Lost His Cloak, which Uncle Toby would like to play if he could. But alas, although their names survive in many ancient books, no one ever took the trouble to write down how they were played!

Charades

Would Christmas be complete without charades? Uncle Toby is so sure it wouldn't that he keeps a trunk full of costumes adaptable to practically any character his guests might need. Here is an amusing interlude to be slipped in between two sets of the game.

Three guests, chosen because they are best known to everyone present, are in on the scheme beforehand. When their turn comes to go out, they announce that part of their **To the Ancient Sport of Pantomime Is Added a Bit of a Surprise** charade demands a pencil and paper for each of those remaining, then they retire to dress in bright-coloured costumes. Suddenly there is a scramble at the door. In dashes X in a red shirt and stocking cap, pursued by Y, who brandishes a pint milk-bottle above a plumed 1890 hat set rakishly on his head. Z follows, hatless but draped in a Persian shawl. Z, with a howl, grabs the bottle from Y, makes a pass at X, who drops, rolls over, leaps up, and bolts from the room with the others hot on his trail.

Now, when the din has subsided, everyone must write down exactly what happened, describing action and sound and the clothing worn by each of the three. At the end of five minutes the written evidence is gathered up to be read. And, oh, the vagaries of the mind and eye! Almost everyone will agree, for instance, that all three shouted throughout the scuffle, though as a matter of fact only Z made a sound. Two reports may wrongly give Z a hat, and only about half will identify the weapon brandished at X.

Story by the Minute

As the last game of all Uncle Toby proposes an impromptu Christmas continued story. The person sitting on his right starts the story, making it up as he goes along. At the end of one minute he is stopped and the neighbour at *his* right continues, adding new characters and adventures. The beginning may be anything from "A mysterious old gentleman looking a good deal like Santa Claus walked . . ." to "Napoleon drew up his guard on the morning of December 25th and said. . . ."

Uncle Toby Has the Last and Best Word of This One

By the time the circle is completed a fabulous yarn will have been constructed. Uncle Toby's job is to give it an ending—which is always a happy one and which always leads up to his reading the story of the Cratchits' Christmas goose (see pages 96-100). And this is his signal that festivities for the day are over, God bless them every one.

6

Uncle Toby's Idea of What Makes the
Perfect Christmas Dinner, and How
to Go About Preparing It. He Took a
Good Deal of Interest in This Section.

PREPARING THE CHRISTMAS DINNER

What a thankless thing it seems to be called away from holly wreaths and candles, from Tiny Tim and Bethlehem, from all the games and fun of the season—out into the kitchen! Of course the results of our efforts will be their own reward—exclamations of delight from all the family, a jolly, comfortable meal, followed by that unmistakable yet delightful feeling of being unable ever to swallow another mouthful. . . . And before the coffee and nuts, the younger children, stuffed fuller than ever was any turkey, will have to be carried, asleep, from the table for their afternoon naps.

A Word to the Maker of the Feast, Who Is Advised to Read Further

What has gone on in the kitchen to produce such an effect? Uncle Toby, being of an experimental nature, has worked out a few schemes which may help to make the principal meal of the day a little more exciting—and he may be able to give a suggestion or two which will simplify things for those who delight in playing host to a large company on Christmas Day.

What is the Christmas dinner to be? There are, of course, plenty of local variations. But to English-speaking people Christmas dinners are pretty much of a pattern, of which Uncle Toby's version goes something like this:

SOUP (IF YOU MUST!)
Cream of tomato, or
Cream of mushroom, or
Mock turtle
GARNISHES:
Celery—Olives—Salted Nuts

ROAST:
Turkey with cranberry sauce, or
Goose with apple sauce, or
Suckling pig with apple sauce
VEGETABLES:
Potatoes (*white:* mashed or riced; *sweet:* baked or candied)
Winter squash
Beets
Turnips
Boiled or creamed onions (no choice about the
onions themselves—you have to have them!)
DESSERTS:
Plum pudding
Mince pie
Pumpkin pie (or Squash)
Ice cream
BREADS AND CAKES:
Beaten biscuit
Raisin bread
Parker House rolls
Fruit cake
Christmas cookies
Spice cakes

Uncle Toby feels very strongly that salads and entrées just don't fit into this pattern. Of course there is no legislation against them, any more than there is against serving roast lamb and apricot mousse as Christmas fare. But Christmas is after all a day of traditions, not of innovations.

Uncle Toby Makes a Confession of Prejudice and Gives a Hint About Good Planning

For the modern housewife, in a restricted kitchen, any real Christmas dinner is out of the question without planning and doing for two or three days beforehand. What can be prepared before the day itself? A surprisingly large part of the meal.

The *Tomato or Mushroom stock, of course without
milk or cream
The celery

The stuffing (keep dry)

*Cranberry sauce

*Apple sauce

Potatoes and other vegetables washed and/or peeled
    (keep peeled potatoes covered with cold water)

*Plum pudding

*Mince pie

Pumpkin pie (sieved pumpkin can be bought in cans)

Custard for *ice cream

If all these things have been made ready beforehand, the work
on the day itself will be quite simple:

(1) Heat and blend the soup.

(2) Stuff and roast the meat.

(3) Cook vegetables.

(4) Warm plum pudding or mince pie. Freeze ice cream, if
     you mean to make it at home. (This can, of course, be
     done late Christmas Eve, or early Christmas morning.)

So much for planning the work. Now a few comments on each
of the traditional dishes.

Cream of Tomato Soup. Use half as much tomato stock as you
will need (any standard brand of canned tomato soup will serve

**Give Special
Heed to These
Preludes to the
Big Dinner**

excellently; if you want to make it at home,
follow a cook-book recipe for clear tomato soup)
—the other half being milk (with as much
cream as you like added). Heat separately
and mix *just* before serving. Don't forget
that a little baking-soda added to the tomato prevents
curdling.

Cream of Mushroom Soup is best made with clear meat stock.
A small can of chicken consommé will suffice for enough soup to
serve eight people. Boil your mushrooms (whole, skins, stems, or
dried) in the meat stock (with water as needed) until soft. Allow
two ounces of mushroom (or the stems and peelings from four
ounces) for each portion—more if you want a richer soup. When
the mushrooms are soft, put through a collander, carefully pre-
serving all the liquid. When you wish to serve, add this liquid to

---

* All starred items *can* safely be bought in canned or ready-prepared form.
But all except the tomato stock, mince meat, and plum pudding are more wisely
made at home.

the heated stock with an equal quantity of light cream (separately heated) or milk, thickened with a little flour, exactly as you would a white (cream) sauce.

Croûtons. Use white bread, dice it *small* (one-quarter to three-eighths of an inch). Fry it in very hot butter, quickly until dark. Drain on paper. Serve at once, ten to twelve pieces in each serving of soup.

Roast Turkey and Stuffing. There is no use talking about the actual roasting except this general advice: start hot and then cool off—and allow fifteen to twenty minutes for each pound. But the stuffing—there's another story! A turkey has a mild-flavoured meat. Therefore you shouldn't put too much of any ingredient in the dressing which has a strong flavour of its own.

Some people put currants and raisins and walnuts and even prunes in their turkey stuffing. Uncle Toby doesn't.

The basis of all stuffings is bread. The amount of bread depends on the size of the bird—anything from one to four loaves. Use a big bowl for mixing. Break up about twice as much stale bread as you think you'll need, judging by the size of the cavity to be filled. Fry a pound of sausage very brown and crisp. Drain. Break up and add to bread. (One pound of sausage to ten pounds of turkey. Link or meat.) Peel and blanch about three-quarters of a pound of chestnuts (for a ten-pound bird), break up and add to bread and sausage. Chop about two handfuls of peeled onions in a meat grinder, catching all the juice in a saucer, and add to previous ingredients. Stir well. If you are working beforehand, put this mixture aside until you are starting to roast the turkey.

> Uncle Toby Feels That if Feasts Had Never Existed It Would Have Been Necessary to Invent 'em When Stuffed Turkey Was Discovered

When you are ready for the oven, put enough boiling water into the mixture described above to make it like a mud pie. Flavor with salt, pepper, and sage to taste (a little sage goes a long way). Stuff your bird carefully, keeping the gizzard, liver, and heart *out*.

Then—roast the animal, basting as often as you can. (Don't forget! *Water in the pan!*) About twenty minutes before serving, boil the gizzard and heart. Chop both in little pieces, discarding skin and membranes. Chop up the liver, after blanching in any convenient boiling water for ninety seconds. Take the fowl out of its metal nest, placing it on the platter. Look at what's left. If it's mostly grease, pour about two tablespoonfuls onto a frying-pan. Discard the rest of the grease. Whatever is then left in the pan, *preserve it*! Pour water from the kettle onto it, and let it be for a while. In the interim, put a tablespoon (rounded) of flour into the two tablespoons of grease already in the frying-pan (if there wasn't that much grease to begin with, you will have to add bacon fat or butter to make up the amount). Stir the flour and fat until the mixture is a little better than golden brown. Add gradually the (drained) watery liquid from the turkey pan, or, if necessary, water from the kettle, stirring continuously, until you have a gravy. Add the chopped gizzard, heart, and liver. A half-glass of strained orange juice will help a lot, and there you are—stuffed turkey with giblet gravy.

Roast Goose. Goose is coarser in flavor than turkey, which means that you can put anything you want into the dressing— raisins, currants, candied peel, etc. Otherwise the **Look Carefully** recipe for stuffing is the same. When you make **at the Sugges-** the gravy, expect the pan juice to be much greasier. **tion for Gravy** In an ordinary goose there'll be enough extra fat **Given Here** for a making of soap over and above what you need for gravy—or would have been in the days when soap was made at home. Two ideas about goose or duck: use orange juice instead of hot water in your basting-pan; put a dozen olives, cut into small pieces, into the pan with goose. Put the slightly pressed sections of four or five oranges and the sliced pieces of twelve olives into the giblet gravy of a goose or duck.

Suckling Pig. Easy enough—but consult a cook-book about apples, paper-cuffs, glazing, etc. Stuffing as for a turkey. Cook twenty minutes to the pound.

Cranberry Sauce. Some like it natural, some strained. In any case use pound for pound of cooked berries and sugar (a measuring-cup will do very well). Let the water be a minimum. If the berries burn, don't be too worried—it has little effect upon the flavour. Of course the sugar isn't added till the berries are cooked.

Apple Sauce. Cook the apples first with a slice of lemon. Use very little water in your pan and keep it covered. Strain. Add sugar to taste and boil up once. Grate a little nutmeg over all.

Potatoes (white). There is very little to be said here. Mashed need salt, pepper, cream, and butter. Riced require a little chopped parsley.

Sauces and Vegetables— Those Minor But Vastly Important Satellites

Potatoes (sweet). If you want to candy them, cook them first (boiled or baked). Then slice when cold. Fry slices in plenty of butter, putting in lots of white sugar. Don't worry about how hot the pan gets—the hotter the better, short of red hot. The same thing can be done in a glass dish in a hot oven.

Winter Squash is either baked, in convenient sections with a small slice of bacon, salt, and pepper; or boiled and puréed with an equal quantity of mashed potatoes.

Beets are boiled in their skins until soft, then skinned.

Turnips. Boil until soft. Mash and add equal amount of mashed potato. Season (butter, salt, pepper). Not quite as good as mashed potato, but different.

Onions. The big thing after boiling them is to get them well drained. Otherwise the butter (or cream sauce) will part company with the onions and the result will be unsightly.

Plum Pudding. Easy! Buy one and heat it in the can! (See below the recipe Uncle Toby uses, if you prefer to make it yourself.) Hard sauce is one-half granulated or confectioners' sugar, one-half *sweet* butter, well beaten together. Add at the end rum or brandy to taste. Cover with ground nutmeg.

If Cans for Christmas Be Heresy They Are Atoned for Below

Mince Pie. Buy mincemeat (or see Uncle Toby's recipe at the end!) Make ordinary pie crust. Bake pie with mincemeat in it. Warm before serving, if you prefer.

Pumpkin Pie. Either boil the flesh of a pumpkin until soft, discarding the rind and seeds, or buy a can of sieved pumpkin. To one-and-one-half cups of pumpkin flesh strained through a collander until it is perfectly smooth add three-quarters of a cup of brown sugar, one teaspoonful of ground cinnamon, one-half

And Last of All, Five Full Recipes Tested by Uncle Toby for the More Difficult of the Desserts, All Better Made at Home

teaspoonful of ground ginger, and a little salt. Separate two eggs. Add yolks to mixture described above. Beat whites stiff. Add at end with two cups of milk. Place mixture, well stirred, in pie crust and place in *hot* oven until brown on top. Then slow the oven down until done. These quantities should be doubled for a large pie.

Ice Cream. There are two kinds of ice cream: (1) *French.* Make a custard. Three egg yolks, one-half cup of sugar. Put some grated vanilla bean or vanilla extract with one pint milk. Scald milk with vanilla bean. Add gradually to beaten egg yolks and sugar. When cool, add beaten whites, and a half-pint of cream (whipped stiff). Makes a little over one quart. (2) *Philadelphia or American.* To a given quantity of sweetened fruit pulp (not citrus) or flavored milk (chocolate, coffee, caramel, vanilla) add an equal quantity of cream and freeze.

Remember in freezing ice cream that the salt—not the ice—is the essential, and that the salt cannot operate without water. Once you have water and ice and salt all together, then the cream will freeze very quickly.

Now—just in case you are wondering how it's done—here are three recipes you might like to try if you have the courage: *Mincemeat—plum pudding—Christmas cake.* These are *not easy.* For the rest of the dinner Uncle Toby feels he can almost be responsible, so long as you follow directions carefully. But as for these last three things—he guarantees nothing, though he assures you that the recipes have been frequently tested and the results approved.

Mincemeat. Ingredients: One pound of finely-chopped suet, one pound of currants washed and picked, one pound of raisins stoned and quartered, one pound of chopped apples, one pound of granulated sugar, one-half pound of seedless raisins, one-quarter pound of shredded mixed candied citron, lemon and orange peel, two lemons, one-half gill of brandy, one-half saltspoonful each of nutmeg, mace, and cinnamon. *Method:* Pare the lemons thinly, simmer the rinds in a little water until perfectly tender, then pound them or rub them through a fine sieve. Mix all the ingredients well together, press into a jar, cover closely, and keep in a cool, dry place for at least one month before using. *Time:* About one hour. Sufficient for four or five pounds of mincemeat.

Plum Pudding. Ingredients: Eight ounces of moist sugar, eight ounces of finely-chopped suet, eight ounces of seedless raisins, eight ounces of raisins halved and stoned, eight ounces of currants washed and dried, four ounces of shredded mixed candied peel, four ounces of flour, four ounces of bread crumbs, two ounces of almonds blanched and shredded, the grated rind of one lemon, three eggs, a saltspoonful of nutmeg grated, one-half teaspoonful of salt, one-quarter of a pint of milk, one small wineglassful of brandy (optional). *Method:* Mix all the dry ingredients together, stir in the well-beaten eggs, milk, and brandy (if used), turn the mixture into two well-greased basins, steam from five to six hours. Sufficient for eight to nine persons.

Christmas Cake No. 1. Ingredients: Half a pound of butter, half a pound of granulated sugar, half a pound of seedless raisins, half a pound of currants, six ounces of mixed candied peel, one pound of flour, quarter ounce baking-powder, four eggs, milk. *Method:* Sieve the baking-powder two or three times with the flour onto a sheet of paper to mix well. Put the butter and the sugar into a clean pan and stand in front of the fire to soften. Weigh the fruit and add to the flour, having carefully cleaned and picked them free from stalks and stones. Cut up the peel into thin shreds, and mix it with the fruit and flour. Break the eggs into a clean basin. Now proceed to beat up the butter and sugar into a cream, add the eggs one at a time, beating well after each addition of egg. When all are in, add the flour and fruit, moisten to the usual cake batter consistency with milk, and bake in round or square well-papered and greased tins. This will make nearly four pounds of cake, and can be baked in one or more cakes as desired. *Time:* From three to four hours to bake, in a slow oven.

King Arthur's Christmas Feast

They served up salmon, venison, and wild boars,
By hundreds, and by dozens, and by scores.
Hogsheads of honey, kilderkins of mustard,
Muttons, and fatted beeves, and bacon swine;
Herons and bitterns, peacocks, swan, and bustard,

Teal, mallard, pigeons, widgeons, and in fine,
Plum puddings, pancakes, apple pies, and custard.
And therewithal they drank good Gascon wine,
With mead, and ale, and cider of our own;
For porter, punch, and negus were not known.

7

Before and After and With the Meal,
Uncle Toby, as You Might Expect,
Recommends Appetizing Beverages
for Every Taste and Every Guest.

WHAT TO DRINK BEFORE, DURING, AND AFTER THE CHRISTMAS DINNER

In Uncle Toby's opinion, no gin should be produced at any Christmas festivity, nor any vodka, nor any fancy cocktails, nor any weird liquors with funny foreign names. **On the Outstanding Virtue of Sherry to Whet the Christmas Appetite** What he really means is that, although Christmas drinks should have colour, they should be of sound and simple composition. If some of the younger members of the family home from college for the holidays want to shake up Pink Ladies in the pantry, Uncle Toby is tolerant. But for himself there is only one proper appetizer—a glass of sherry. If mock-turtle soup is being served, or any clear soup, a bottle of sherry will also be found on the table to be added to the served soup as desired.

About the cheeriest *looking* Christmas drink, thinks Uncle Toby, is Cranberry Crush. He recommends it especially for the youngsters and for anyone else who wants mild before-dinner sipping. So there's always a tall pitcher of this in the ice-box:

Put two quarts of water to boil with a table-
    spoonful of oatmeal and a bit of lemon peel.
Mash one cup of fresh cranberries in a cup of
    cold water. **What to Put in the Children's Glasses — a Problem Solved**
Add the mashed cranberries to the boiling water,
    boil thirty minutes, and sweeten to taste.
Then strain and cool.

It's best not to get this too sweet, lest you dull the sharp cranberry flavor.

When dinner really gets started, Uncle Toby outdoes himself in variety of bottles. Only two things are barred from the Christmas board—highballs and punches. Neither of these goes with food. Some of the menfolk will prefer ale, some cider. And the drinkers of cranberry crush before dinner will surely be having sweet cider now. Uncle Toby himself is **Wine for the Goose, Wine for the Gander** partial to good wines—but none of this hifalutin' business about a different wine with each course. "No *Sir*," pronounces the Old Gentleman, stabbing the air with a prodigious drumstick. "Take one good wine—whatever you like—and stick with it right through dinner. Everybody knows that the only proper wine to drink with turkey and goose is a still, white wine, and with game and roast suckling pig a still, dry red wine. So the sideboard holds a great array of red and white wines, none of them fancy, but all good sound juice of the grape. The white wines are served fresh from the ice-box, the red at room temperature or warmer.

Uncle Toby doesn't think much of champagne as a *table* wine, so he doesn't serve it during the meal. Champagne is a *sipping* and a *toasting* wine (the one beverage which even the most careful mothers, on great occasions, sometimes let their children sip). That's why it comes with the dessert, and why it really doesn't conflict with the firm principle of sticking to your one favourite *table* wine all through the meal. The first few drops of the champagne are poured into Uncle Toby's own tall, thin-stemmed glass, for he is the host. Then everybody else's glass is filled before his own gets its full share.

The Time for Champagne — and a Toast That Goes Round the Table

Now comes a great business of drinking toasts in the champagne. The first toast is always to Uncle Toby himself, and by custom in the household, is always proposed by the smallest little tyke who is able to clamber upon a chair with a tiny drop of champagne in his glass, and say, "Here's to Uncle Toby!" Then all the way around the table, one by one, with toasts to each other and the weather and the cook and the wine and Santa Claus, until it's finally Uncle

Toby's turn to propose the last toast. His eyes are always a trifle moist as he rises to his feet and, holding his glass high above the table, repeats the grandest old toast of all, first made years ago by Tiny Tim, "God bless us—every one!"

Now Uncle Toby asks all the womenfolk if they will have some cordial, such as Crême de Menthe or Benedictine or Cointreau— just a thimbleful, to settle the stomach. A bottle of vintage port is uncorked for the men who wish it, and one of brandy for the others. The coffee is there, black, fragrant, and steaming. Cigars pass round. Uncle Toby inhales the aroma of his brandy deeply, cupping the thin, big-bellied glass in his two hands to warm the liquor so that its perfume may rise in more abundance. And thus the Christmas feast drifts blissfully to its end.

THE WASSAIL BOWL

The Wassail Bowl Brought Up to Date Uncle Toby usually makes this a Christmas Eve occasion rather than Christmas Day. He has devised his own modification of a traditional Wassail recipe, suited to the modern palate, but he still retains the ancient name:

One Yard of Flannel

Heat one quart of ale almost to the boiling-point.

Into it stir some grated nutmeg, powdered ginger, and the peel of one lemon.

While the ale is heating, beat up three eggs with four ounces of moistened white sugar.

Then put the hot ale into the beaten sugar-and-eggs in one pitcher, and into another put a quart of good old rum or brandy.

Turn these ingredients back and forth from one pitcher into another until the mixture is smooth, then pour into the holly-wreathed Wassail Bowl. Heat all containers thoroughly beforehand, else the mixture will be tepid.

The secret of this mixture's authority, says Uncle Toby, is two-fold: the age and quality of the rum or brandy, and heat. To keep it hot Uncle Toby insists on hot pitchers and a hot bowl. Of course one makes several batches, rather than preparing all before-hand and running the risk of having it cool.

EGGNOGS AND PUNCHES FOR CHRISTMAS AFTERNOON AND
EVENING

Christmas afternoon and night are the great visiting times, when everybody calls on Uncle Toby to give him the season's best wishes—this usually in the evening—and when Uncle Toby calls on everybody to do the same—this usually in the afternoon. On these peregrinations it always seems, oddly enough, that the punch or eggnog he is imbibing at the moment is the best he has ever tasted, and he immediately requires that his host give him the recipe. Here are a few of his finds, both hot and cold. He has tried every one of them, conscientiously, and can recommend all, as specified, except the recipe in rhyme, which he never had the courage to attempt.

Old Louisville Eggnog—for those who like a relatively liquid eggnog.

Six eggs; one and one-half cups white sugar; one quart Bourbon whisky; one-half pint Jamaica rum; one quart whipped cream; one pint straight cream; one pint vanilla ice cream. Beat the eggs separately, holding out for the moment the whites of three eggs. Add some sugar, now, and beat up stiff with a silver fork. Then add the whisky, the rum, whipped cream, and nutmeg. The three egg whites you held out, now beat up and put on top of all the rest. Leave in a cool place overnight, pour the pint of straight cream into it in the morning. When you're ready to serve it, float the ice cream on top. These quantities are for a large company; reduce as required.

Three Different Eggnogs, Frothy, Fluid and Firm, Ice-Cream Being the Secret of One of Them

Old Virginia Eggnog—for those who prefer a frothy eggnog, not too strong.

Beat up two eggs, leaving out the white of one, with one-quarter cup white sugar. Beat them hard and well, then add one-quarter cup (good measure) of the very best old Kentucky whisky. Mix this well, then add one cup of the thickest Jersey cream. Take the one remaining egg white and beat it stiff, put one teaspoon of sugar into it, then add it to the main part of the nog, and stir it in.

Kentucky Eggnog—for two people, and moderately frothy.

Two eggs; four tablespoonfuls rye whisky; two tablespoons Jamaica rum; two and one-half level tablespoons sugar; three tablespoons whipped cream. Beat the egg yolks very light, add whisky and rum slowly, still beating. Beat the whites with the sugar until smooth and stiff. Combine the two mixtures, fold in whipped cream, reserving a little to dot on top of each glass.

Cider Cup

Into a saucepan put the rind of one lemon, cut very thin, one cup of boiling water, eight to ten lumps of sugar, one pint of sherry or Madeira, one pint of Malaga wine, two bottles of clear cider. Heat this to just under the boiling point, flavour with borage (though this is not essential), and serve hot.

Lighter Drinks Including the Punches — Hot and Cold

Virginia Punch—for those liking a light punch.

Put a large block of ice into the punch bowl and over it pour the juice of six lemons and six oranges, one quart of good claret, two quarts of extra dry champagne. (American vintages are quite adequate.) Put in four slices of fresh pineapple and four slices of orange with the peel on. Garnish with fresh mint and sweeten as needed.

Old English Rum Punch—hot.

Juice of three lemons; grated rind of two lemons; one-half pint of brandy; one and one-half cups of rum; one cup of sugar; one quart of boiling water; nutmeg. Pour the lemon juice over the sugar and add the grated rind. Then mix with the brandy and rum, add the boiling water, let it simmer for two minutes and serve hot.

Rum Punch—cold—especially recommended for large mixed parties where young and old are together.

Twelve lumps of sugar rubbed patiently against the outsides of fresh oranges, until they are thoroughly impregnated with the oil of the fruit; three cups of fruit juices made up of orange, lemon, and canned pineapple in approximately equal parts;

three scant cups of Jamaica rum (Haitian or Louisiana may
be substituted, but *not* Bacardi); four and one-half cups pale
dry ginger ale; one and one-half cups carbonated water. Dissolve sugar in fruit juice, add other ingredients, and pour over
large cake of ice in punch bowl. Don't be discouraged when
rubbing the sugar against the oranges (the same oranges may
be used for juice); it makes all the difference. A small amount
of crushed pineapple may be added. These quantities make
punch for thirty ordinary servings.

Mulled Wine

First, dear madam, you must take
Nine eggs, which carefully you'll break;   **To Be Tested**
Into a bowl you'll drop the white,   **By a Bolder**
The yolks into another by it.   **Soul Than**
  Uncle Toby
Let Betsy beat the whites with switch,
Till they appear quite frothed and rich;
Another hand the yolks must beat
With sugar, which will make them sweet.
Three or four spoonfuls maybe'll do,
Though some perhaps would take but two.
Into a skillet next you'll pour
A bottle of good wine, or more;
Put half a pint of water, too,
Or it may prove too strong for you.
And while the eggs by two are beating,
The wine and water may be heating;
But when it comes to boiling heat,
The yolks and whites together beat
With half a pint of water more,
Mixing them well, then gently pour
Into the skillet with the wine,
And stir it briskly all the time.
Then pour it off into a pitcher,
Grate nutmeg in to make it richer,
Then drink it hot, for he's a fool
Who lets such precious liquor cool.

. . ..

Many years ago Uncle Toby experimented with a traditional recipe for the Wassail Bowl, which was said to be at least as old as King Canute and is certainly just as improbable. First dissolve one pound of raw sugar (Uncle Toby thought this meant *brown sugar*), in one quart of warm beer. Into this grate some nutmeg and sprinkle a bit of powdered ginger. Then add four tumblers of sherry and two more quarts of warm beer. This all goes into the big bowl, which is wreathed round with holly. The final touches are three slices of lemon and three slices of toasted bread, which float on the surface. After one taste of this flat and tepid fluid, Uncle Toby gave it as his opinion that King Canute would have done better to turn back the Wassail Bowl than the ocean. In fact, as Uncle Toby afterwards discovered, the knights of old didn't drink this stuff, either. It may have been prepared by some particularly parsimonious lord of the manor for his peasant farmers and his servants,

A Wassail Bowl of Other Days, to Which No Guarantees Are Attached

who may all have got together on Christmas Eve outside his door and sung a few songs, something on this order:

> *A jolly Wassail Bowl,*
> *A Wassail of good ale,*
> *Well fare the butler's soul,*
> *That setteth this to stale,*
> *Our Jolly Wassail.*
>
> *Our Wassail we do fill*
> *With apples and with spice,*
> *Then grant us your good will*
> *To taste here once or twice*
> *Of our Wassail.*
>
> *Much joy betide you all,*
> *Our prayers shall be still,*
> *We hope and ever shall*
> *For this, your great good will—*
> *To our Wassail.*

Then they presumably gave a hip, hip, hurray for the lord, who was expecting it, but was nevertheless so gratified that he added a little more warm beer to the Wassail Bowl. Then it was his turn to sing, and flinging open the front door he let go with the following:

> *Come, bring with a noise,*
> *My merry, merry boys,*
> *The Christmas log to the firing,*
> *While my good dame, she*
> *Bids ye all be free,*
> *And drink to your heart's desiring.*
> *Drink now the strong beer,*
> *Cut the white loaf here,*
> *The while the meat is a-shredding;*
> *For the rare mince pie*
> *And the plums stand by,*
> *To fill the paste that's a-kneading!*

After that effort, the lord was certainly badly in need of something more than warm beer, but Uncle Toby never could find out what it was he took. Instead, he devised his own Wassail Bowl for which you already have the recipe as "One Yard of Flannel" (page 196).

8

Because He Has a Particular Affection for Children, Uncle Toby Has Made a Special Selection of Unusual Christmas Tales for Boys and Girls.

Christmas Every Day

By William Dean Howells

THE little girl came into her papa's study, as she always did
Saturday morning before breakfast, and asked for a story.
He tried to beg off that morning, for he was very busy, but she
would not let him. So he began:

"Well, once there was a little pig ——"

She put her hand over his mouth and stopped him at the word.
She said she had heard little-pig stories till she was perfectly
sick of them.

"Well, what kind of story shall I tell, then?"

"About Christmas. It's getting to be the season. It's past
Thanksgiving already."

"It seems to me," her papa argued, "that I've told as often
about Christmas as I have about little pigs."

"No difference! Christmas is more interesting."

"Well!" Her papa roused himself from his writing by a great
effort. "Well, then, I'll tell you about the little girl that wanted it
Christmas every day in the year. How would you like that?"

"First rate!" said the little girl; and she nestled into comfortable shape in his lap, ready for listening.

"Very well, then, this little pig—Oh, what are you pounding
me for?"

"Because you said little pig instead of little girl."

"I should like to know what's the difference between a little
pig and a little girl that wanted it Christmas every day!"

"Papa," said the little girl, warningly, "if you don't go on,
I'll give it to you!" And at this her papa darted off like lightning,
and began to tell the story as fast as he could:

Well, once there was a little girl who liked Christmas so much
that she wanted it to be Christmas every day in the year; and as
soon as Thanksgiving was over she began to send postal cards to

Copyright 1892 by Harper and Brothers, copyright 1919 by W. D. Howells.

204

the old Christmas Fairy to ask if she mightn't have it. But the old Fairy never answered any of the postals; and after a while the little girl found out that the Fairy was pretty particular, and wouldn't notice anything but letters—not even correspondence cards in envelopes; but real letters on sheets of paper, and sealed outside with a monogram—or your initial, anyway. So, then, she began to send her letters; and in about three weeks—or just the day before Christmas, it was—she got a letter from the Fairy, saying she might have it Christmas every day for a year, and then they would see about having it longer.

The little girl was a good deal excited already, preparing for the old-fashioned, once-a-year Christmas that was coming the next day, and perhaps the Fairy's promise didn't make such an impression on her as it would have made at some other time. She just resolved to keep it to herself, and surprise everybody with it as it kept coming true; and then it slipped out of her mind altogether.

She had a splendid Christmas. She went to bed early, so as to let Santa Claus have a chance at the stockings, and in the morning she was up the first of anybody and went and felt them, and found hers all lumpy with packages of candy, and oranges and grapes, and pocket-books and rubber balls, and all kinds of small presents, and her big brother's with nothing but the tongs in them, and her young-lady sister's with a new silk umbrella, and her papa's and mamma's with potatoes and pieces of coal wrapped up in tissue-paper, just as they always had every Christmas. Then she waited around till the rest of the family were up, and she was the first to burst into the library, when the doors were opened, and look at the large presents laid out on the library table—books, and portfolios, and boxes of stationery, and breastpins, and dolls, and little stoves, and dozens of handkerchiefs, and inkstands, and skates, and snow-shovels, and photograph-frames, and little easels, and boxes of water-colors, and Turkish paste, and nougat, and candied cherries, and dolls' houses, and water-proofs—and the big Christmas tree, lighted and standing in a waste-basket in the middle.

She had a splendid Christmas all day. She ate so much candy that she did not want any breakfast; and the whole forenoon the presents kept pouring in that the expressman had not had time to deliver the night before; and she went round giving the presents she had got for other people, and came home and ate turkey and cranberry for dinner, and plum pudding and nuts and raisins and oranges and more candy, and then went out and coasted, and came in with a stomach-ache, crying; and her papa said he would see if his house was turned into that sort of fool's paradise another year; and they had a light supper, and pretty early everybody went to bed cross.

Here the little girl pounded her papa in the back again.
"Well, what now? Did I say pigs?"
"You made them act like pigs."
"Well, didn't they?"
"No matter; you oughtn't to put it into a story."
"Very well, then, I'll take it all out."
Her father went on:

The little girl slept very heavily, and she slept very late, but she was wakened at last by the other children dancing round her bed with their stockings full of presents in their hands.
"What is it?" said the little girl, and she rubbed her eyes and tried to rise up in bed.
"Christmas! Christmas! Christmas!" they all shouted, and waved their stockings.
"Nonsense! It was Christmas yesterday."
Her brothers and sisters just laughed.
"We don't know about that. It's Christmas today, anyway. You come into the library and see."
Then all at once it flashed on the little girl that the Fairy was keeping her promise, and her year of Christmases was beginning. She was dreadfully sleepy, but she sprang up like a lark—a lark that had overeaten itself and gone to bed cross—and darted into the library. There it was again! Books, and portfolios, and boxes of stationery, and breastpins ——

"You needn't go over it all, papa; I guess I can remember just what was there," said the little girl.

Well, and there was the Christmas tree blazing away, and the family picking out their presents, but looking pretty sleepy, and her father perfectly puzzled, and her mother ready to cry. "I'm sure I don't see how I'm to dispose of all these things," said her mother, and her father said it seemed to him they had had something just like it the day before, but he supposed he must have dreamed it. This struck the little girl as the best kind of a joke; and so she ate so much candy she didn't want any breakfast, and went round carrying presents, and had turkey and cranberry for dinner, and then went out and coasted, and came in with a ——

"Papa!"

"Well, what now?"

"What did you promise, you forgetful thing?"

"Oh! oh yes!"

Well, the next day, it was just the same thing over again, but everybody getting crosser; and at the end of a week's time so many people had lost their tempers that you could pick up lost tempers anywhere; they perfectly strewed the ground. Even when people tried to recover their tempers they usually got somebody else's, and it made the most dreadful mix.

The little girl began to get frightened, keeping the secret all to herself; she wanted to tell her mother, but she didn't dare to; and she was ashamed to ask the Fairy to take back her gift, it seemed ungrateful and ill-bred, and she thought she would try to stand it, but she hardly knew how she could, for a whole year. So it went on and on, and it was Christmas on St. Valentine's Day and Washington's Birthday, just the same as any day, and it didn't skip even the First of April, though everything was counterfeit that day, and that was some little relief.

After a while coal and potatoes began to be awfully scarce, so many had been wrapped up in tissue-paper to fool papas and mommas with. Turkeys got to be about a thousand dollars apiece ——

"Papa!"

"Well, what?"

"You're beginning to fib."

"Well, two thousand, then."

And they got to passing off almost anything for turkeys—half-grown humming-birds, and even rocs out of the *Arabian Nights* —the real turkeys were so scarce. And cranberries—well, they asked a diamond apiece for cranberries. All the woods and orchards were cut down for Christmas trees, and where the woods and orchards used to be it looked just like a stubble-field, with the stumps. After a while they had to make Christmas trees out of rags, and stuff them with bran, like old-fashioned dolls; but there were plenty of rags, because people got so poor, buying presents for one another, that they couldn't get any new clothes, and they just wore their old ones to tatters. They got so poor that everybody had to go to the poorhouse, except the confectioners, and the fancy-store keepers, and the picture-book sellers, and the expressmen; and they all got so rich and proud that they would hardly wait upon a person when he came to buy. It was perfectly shameful!

Well, after it had gone on about three or four months, the little girl, whenever she came into the room in the morning and saw those great ugly, lumpy stockings dangling at the fireplace, and the disgusting presents around everywhere, used to just sit down and burst out crying. In six months she was perfectly exhausted; she couldn't even cry any more; she just lay on the lounge and rolled her eyes and panted. About the beginning of October she took to sitting down on dolls whenever she found them—French dolls, or any kind—she hated the sight of them so; and by Thanksgiving she was crazy, and just slammed her presents across the room.

By that time people didn't carry presents around nicely any more. They flung them over the fence, or through the window, or anything; and, instead of running their tongues out and taking great pains to write "For dear Papa," or "Mamma," or "Brother," or "Sister," or "Susie," or "Sammie," or "Billie," or "Bobbie," or "Jimmie," or "Jennie," or whoever it was, and troubling to get the spelling right, and then signing their names, they used to write in the gift-books, "Take it, you horrid old thing!" and then go and bang it against the front door. Nearly everybody had built barns to hold their presents, but pretty soon the barns overflowed, and then they used to let them lie out in the rain, or anywhere. Sometimes the police used to come and tell them to shovel their presents off the sidewalks or they would arrest them.

"I thought you said everybody had gone to the poorhouse," interrupted the little girl.

"They did go, at first," said her papa; "but after a while the poorhouse got so full that they had to send the people back to their own houses. They tried to cry, when they got back, but they couldn't make the least sound."

"Why couldn't they?"

"Because they had lost their voices, saying 'Merry Christmas' so much. Did I tell you how it was on the Fourth of July?"

"No. How was it?" And the little girl nestled closer, in expectation of something uncommon.

Well, the night before, the boys stayed up to celebrate, as they always do, and fell asleep before twelve o'clock, as usual, expecting to be wakened by the bells and cannon. But it was nearly eight o'clock before the first boy in the United States woke up, and then he found out what the trouble was. As soon as he could get his clothes on he ran out of the house and smashed a big cannon-torpedo down on the pavement; but it didn't make any more noise than a damp wad of paper; and after he tried about twenty or thirty more, he began to pick them up and look at them. Every single torpedo was a big raisin! Then he just streaked it upstairs, and examined his fire-crackers and toy pistol and two-dollar collection of fireworks, and found that they were nothing but sugar and candy painted up to look like fireworks! Before ten o'clock every boy in the United States found out that his Fourth of July things had turned into Christmas things; and then they just sat down and cried—they were so mad. There are about twenty million boys in the United States, and so you can imagine what a noise they made. Some men got together before night, with a little powder that hadn't turned into purple sugar yet, and they said they would fire off one cannon, anyway. But the cannon burst into a thousand pieces, for it was nothing but rock-candy, and some of the men nearly got killed. The Fourth of July orations turned into Christmas carols, and when anybody tried to read the Declaration, instead of saying, "When in the course of human events it becomes necessary," he was sure to sing "God Rest Ye Merry, Gentlemen." It was perfectly awful.

The little girl drew a deep sigh of satisfaction.
"And how was it at Thanksgiving?"
Her papa hesitated. "Well, I'm almost afraid to tell you. I'm afraid you'll think it's wicked."
"Well, tell, anyway," said the little girl.

Well, before it came Thanksgiving it had leaked out who had caused all these Christmases. The little girl had suffered so much that she had talked about it in her sleep; and after that hardly anybody would play with her. People just perfectly despised her, because if it had not been for her greediness it wouldn't have happened; and now, when it came Thanksgiving, and she wanted them to go to church, and have squash pie and turkey, and show their gratitude, they said that all the turkeys had been eaten up for her old Christmas dinners, and if she would stop the Christmases, they would see about the gratitude. Wasn't it dreadful! And the very next day the little girl began to send letters to the Christmas Fairy, and then telegrams, to stop it. But it didn't do any good; and then she got to calling at the Fairy's house, but the girl that came to the door always said, "Not at home," or "Engaged," or "At dinner," or something like that; and so it went on till it came to the old once-a-year-Christmas Eve. The little girl fell asleep, and when she woke up in the morning ——

"She found it was all nothing but a dream," suggested the little girl.
"No, indeed!" said her papa. "It was all every bit true!"
"Well, what did she find out, then?"
"Why, that it wasn't Christmas at last, and wasn't ever going to be, any more. Now it's time for breakfast."
The little girl held her papa fast around the neck.
"You sha'n't go if you're going to leave it so!"
"How do you want it left?"

"Christmas once a year."

"All right," said her papa; and he went on again.

Well, there was the greatest rejoicing all over the country, and it extended clear up into Canada. The people met together everywhere, and kissed and cried for joy. The city carts went around and gathered up all the candy and raisins and nuts, and dumped them into the river; and it made the fish perfectly sick; and the whole United States, as far out as Alaska, was one blaze of bonfires, where the children were burning up their gift-books and presents of all kinds. They had the greatest time!

The little girl went to thank the old Fairy because she had stopped its being Christmas, and she said she hoped she would keep her promise and see that Christmas never, never came again. Then the Fairy frowned, and asked her if she was sure she knew what she meant; and the little girl asked her, "Why not?" and the old Fairy said that now she was behaving just as greedily as ever, and she'd better look out. This made the little girl think it all over carefully again, and she said she would be willing to have it Christmas about once in a thousand years; and then she said a hundred, and then she said ten, and at last she got down to one. Then the Fairy said that was the good old way that had pleased people ever since Christmas began, and she was agreed. Then the little girl said, "What're your shoes made of?" and the Fairy said, "Leather." And the little girl said, "Bargain's done forever," and skipped off, and hippity-hopped the whole way home, she was so glad.

"How will that do?" asked the papa.

"First rate!" said the little girl; but she hated to have the story stop, and was rather sober. However, her mamma put her head in at the door, and asked her papa:

"Are you never coming to breakfast? What have you been telling that child?"

"Oh, just a moral tale."

The little girl caught him around the neck again.

"We know! Don't you tell what, papa! Don't you tell what!"

The Voyage of the Wee Red Cap

A Legend of St. Stephen's Eve That David Heard at Dusk-Hour Just Seven Days Before Christmas

By RUTH SAWYER

YE KNOW, laddy," said big Barney, "over in Ireland they're not keeping Christmas the same as ye do here—the poor, I mean. 'Tis generally the day after, St. Stephen's Day, tho' sometimes 'tis St. Stephen's Eve that they manage a bit of a feast and merrymaking. Them that has little shares with them that has less; and afterward the neighbors gather about the turf fire for a story-telling. Aye, many's the strange tale ye will hear over in Ireland on one of them nights. And here's the tale Old Con, the tinker, used for to be telling about his greatuncle Teig—the most close-fisted man in all of Inneskillen."

And here is the tale as Barney retold it and David heard it, as he sat in the window nook of the lodge at dusk-hour just seven days before Christmas.

It was the Eve of St. Stephen, and Teig sat alone by his fire with naught in his cupboard but a pinch of tea and a bare mixing of meal, and a heart inside of him as soft and warm as the ice on the water-bucket outside the door. The turf was near burnt on the hearth—a handful of golden cinders left, just; and Teig took to counting them greedily on his fingers.

"There's one, two, three, an' four an' five," he laughed. "Faith, there be more bits o' real gold hid undther the loose clay in the corner."

It was the truth; and it was the scraping and scrooching for the last piece that had left Teig's cupboard bare of a Christmas dinner.

"Gold is betther nor eatin' an' dthrinkin'. An' if ye have naught to give, there'll be naught asked of ye." And he laughed again.

212

He was thinking of the neighbors, and the doles of food and piggins of milk that would pass over their thresholds that night to the vagabonds and paupers who were sure to come begging. And on the heels of that thought followed another: who would be giving old Shawn his dinner? Shawn lived a stone's-throw from Teig, alone, in a wee tumbled-in cabin; and for a score of years past Teig had stood on the doorstep every Christmas Eve, and, making a hollow of his two hands, had called across the road:

"Hey, there, Shawn, will ye come over for a sup?"

And Shawn had reached for his crutches, there being but one leg to him, and had come.

"Faith," said Teig, trying another laugh, "Shawn can fast for the once; 'twill be all the same in a month's time." And he fell to thinking of the gold again.

A knock came to the door. Teig pulled himself down in his chair where the shadow would cover him, and held his tongue.

"Teig, Teig!" It was the Widow O'Donnelly's voice. "If ye are there, open your door. I have not got the pay for the spriggin' this month, an' the childther are needin' food."

But Teig put the leash on his tongue, and never stirred till he heard the tramp of her feet going on to the next cabin. Then he saw to it that the door was tight barred. Another knock came, and it was a stranger's voice this time:

"The other cabins are filled; not one but has its hearth crowded. Will ye take us in, the two of us? The wind bites mortal sharp; not a morsel o' food have we tasted this day. Masther, will ye take us in?"

But Teig sat on, a-holding his tongue; and the tramp of the strangers' feet passed down the road. Others took their place— small feet, running. It was the miller's wee Cassie, and she called out as she went by:

"Old Shawn's watchin' for ye. Ye'll not be forgettin' him, will ye, Teig?"

And then the child broke into a song, sweet and clear, as she passed down the road:

"Listen, all ye, 'tis the Feast o' St. Stephen,
Mind that ye keep it, this holy even.

Open your door and greet ye the stranger,
For ye mind that the wee Lord had naught but a manger.
                              Mhuire as truagh!

"Feed ye the hungry and rest ye the weary,
This ye must do for the sake of Our Mary.
'Tis well that ye mind—ye who sit by the fire—
That the Lord He was born in a dark and cold byre.
                              Mhuire as truagh!"

Teig put his fingers deep in his ears. "A million murdthering curses on them that won't let me be! Can't a man try to keep what is his without bein' pesthered by them that has only idled and wasted their days?"

And then the strange thing happened: hundreds of wee lights began dancing outside the window, making the room bright; the hands of the clock began chasing each other round the dial, and the bolt of the door drew itself out. Slowly, without a creak or a cringe, the door opened, and in there trooped a crowd of the Good People. Their wee green cloaks were folded close about them, and each carried a rush candle.

Teig was filled with a great wonderment entirely when he saw the fairies, but when they saw him they laughed.

"We are takin' the loan o' your cabin this night, Teig," said they. "Ye are the only man hereabouts with an empty hearth, an' we're needin' one."

Without saying more, they bustled about the room, making ready. They lengthened out the table and spread and set it; more of the Good People trooped in, bringing stools and food and drink. The pipers came last, and they sat themselves around the chimney-piece a-blowing their chanters and trying the drones. The feasting began and the pipers played, and never had Teig seen such a sight in his life. Suddenly a wee man sang out:

"Clip, clap, clip, clap, I wish I had my wee red cap!"

And out of the air there tumbled the neatest cap Teig had ever laid his two eyes on. The wee man clapped it on his head, crying:

"I wish I was in Spain!" And—whist!—up the chimney he went, and away out of sight!

It happened just as I am telling it. Another wee man called for

his cap, and away he went after the first. And then another and another until the room was empty and Teig sat alone again.

"By my soul," said Teig, "I'd like to thravel like that myself! It's a grand savin' of tickets an' baggage; an' ye get to a place before ye've had time to change your mind. Faith, there is no harm done if I thry it."

So he sang the fairies' rhyme and out of the air dropped a wee cap for him. For a moment the wonder had him, but the next he was clapping the cap on his head, crying:

"Spain!"

Then—whist!—up the chimney he went after the fairies, and before he had time to let out his breath he was standing in the middle of Spain, and strangeness all about him.

He was in a great city. The doorways of the houses were hung with flowers and the air was warm and sweet with the smell of them. Torches burned along the streets, sweetmeat-sellers went about crying their wares, and on the steps of a cathedral crouched a crowd of beggars.

"What's the meanin' o' that?" asked Teig of one of the fairies.

"They are waiting for those that are hearing Mass. When they come out they give half of what they have to those that have nothing, so that on this night of all the year there shall be no hunger and no cold."

And then far down the street came the sound of a child's voice, singing:

> "Listen all ye, 'tis the Feast o' St. Stephen,
> Mind that ye keep it, this holy even."

"Curse it!" said Teig. "Can a song fly afther ye?" And then he heard the fairies cry, "Holland!" and he cried, "Holland!" too.

In one leap he was over France, and another over Belgium, and with the third he was standing by long ditches of water frozen fast, and over them glided hundreds upon hundreds of lads and maids. Outside each door stood a wee wooden shoe, empty. Teig saw scores of them as he looked down the ditch of a street.

"What is the meanin' o' those shoes?" he asked the fairies.

"Ye poor lad!" answered the wee man next to him. "Are ye not knowing anything? This is the Gift Night of the year, when every man gives to his neighbor."

A child came to the window of one of the houses, and in her hand was a lighted candle. She was singing as she put the light down close to the glass, and Teig caught the words:

"Open your door and greet ye the stranger,
For ye mind that the wee Lord had naught but a manger.
                            Mhuire as truagh!"

" 'Tis the de'il's work!" cried Teig, and he set the red cap more firmly on his head. "I'm for another country."

I cannot be telling you half of the adventures Teig had that night, nor half the sights that he saw. But he passed by fields that held sheaves of grain for the birds, and doorsteps that held bowls of porridge for the wee creatures. He saw lighted trees, sparkling and heavy with gifts; and he stood outside the churches and watched the crowds pass in, bearing gifts to the Holy Mother and Child.

At last the fairies straightened their caps and cried, "Now for the great hall in the King of England's palace!"

Whist!—and away they went, and Teig after them; and the first thing he knew he was in London, not an arm's-length from the King's throne. It was a grander sight than he had seen in any other country. The hall was filled entirely with lords and ladies; and the great doors were open for the poor and the homeless to come in and warm themselves by the King's fire and feast from the King's table. And many a hungry soul did the King serve with his own hands.

Those that had anything to give gave it in return. It might be a bit of music played on a harp or a pipe, or it might be a dance or a song; but more often it was a wish, just, for good luck and safe-keeping.

Teig was so taken up with the watching that he never heard the fairies when they wished themselves off; moreover, he never saw the wee girl that was fed and went laughing away. But he heard a bit of her song as she passed through the door:

"Feed ye the hungry and rest ye the weary,
This ye must do for the sake of Our Mary."

Then the anger had Teig. "I'll stop your pestherin' tongue once an' for all time!" And, catching the cap from his head, he threw it after her.

No sooner was the cap gone than every soul in the hall saw him. The next moment they were about him, catching at his coat and crying:

"Where is he from? What does he here? Bring him before the King!"

And Teig was dragged along by a hundred hands to the throne where the King sat.

"He was stealing food," cried one.

"He was stealing the King's jewels," cried another.

"He looks evil," cried a third. "Kill him!"

And in a moment all the voices took it up and the hall rang with, "Aye, kill him, kill him!"

Teig's legs took to trembling, and fear put the leash on his tongue; but after a long silence he managed to whisper:

"I have done evil to no one, no one!"

"Maybe," said the King. "But have ye done good? Come, tell us, have ye given aught to any one this night? If ye have, we will pardon ye."

Not a word could Teig say; fear tightened the leash, for he was knowing full well there was no good to him that night.

"Then ye must die," said the King. "Will ye try hanging or beheading?"

"Hanging, please, your Majesty."

The guards came rushing up and carried him off. But as he was crossing the threshold of the hall a thought sprang at him and held him.

"Your Majesty," he called after him, "will ye grant me a last request?"

"I will," said the King.

"Thank ye. There's a wee red cap that I'm mortal fond of, and I lost it awhile ago; if I could be hung with it on I would hang a deal more comfortable."

The cap was found and brought to Teig.

"Clip, clap, clip, clap, for my wee red cap. I wish I was home!" he sang.

Up and over the heads of the dumfounded guard he flew, and —whist!—and away out of sight. When he opened his eyes again, he was sitting close by his own hearth, with the fire burnt low. The hands of the clock were still, the bolt was fixed firm in the door. The fairies' lights were gone, and the only bright thing was the candle burning in old Shawn's cabin across the road.

A running of feet sounded outside, and then the snatch of a song:

> *" 'Tis well that ye mind, ye who sit by the fire,*
> *That the Lord He was born in a dark and cold byre.*
> *Mhuire as truagh!"*

"Wait ye, whoever ye are!" And Teig was away to the corner, digging fast at the loose clay, as the terrier digs at a bone. He filled his hands full of the shining gold, then hurried to the door, unbarring it.

The miller's wee Cassie stood there, peering at him out of the darkness.

"Take those to the Widow O'Donnelly, do ye hear? And take the rest to the store. Ye tell Jamie to bring up all that he has that is eatable and dhrinkable; an' to the neighbors ye say, 'Teig's keepin' the feast this night.' Hurry now!"

Teig stopped a moment on the threshold until the tramp of her feet had died away; then he made a hollow of his two hands and called across the road:

"Hey, there, Shawn, will ye come over for a sup?"

The Little Match Girl

By HANS CHRISTIAN ANDERSEN

I T WAS late on a bitterly cold, snowy, New Year's Eve. A poor little girl was wandering in the dark cold streets; she was bareheaded and barefooted. She certainly had had shoes on when she left home, but they were not much good, for they were so huge. They had last been worn by her mother, and they fell off the poor little girl's feet when she was running across the street to avoid two carriages that were rolling rapidly by. One of the shoes could not be found at all; and the other was picked up by a boy, who ran off with it, saying that it would do for a cradle when he had children of his own. So the poor little girl had to go on with her little bare feet, which were blue with the cold. She carried a quantity of matches in her old apron, and held a packet of them in her hand. Nobody had bought any from her during all the long day; nobody had even given her a copper.

The poor little creature was hungry and perishing with cold, and she looked the picture of misery. The snowflakes fell upon her long yellow hair, which curled so prettily round her face, but she paid no attention to that. Lights were shining from every window, and there was a most delicious odour of roast goose in the streets, for it was New Year's Eve—she could not forget that. She found a protected place where one house projected a little beyond the next one, and here she crouched, drawing up her feet under her, but she was colder than ever. She did not dare to go home, for she had not sold any matches and had not earned a single penny. Her father would beat her; besides, it was almost as cold at home as it was here. They lived in a house where the wind whistled through every crack, although they tried to stuff up the biggest ones with rags and straw. Her tiny hands were almost paralyzed with cold. Oh, if she could only find some way to warm them! Dared she pull one match out of the bundle and strike it on the wall to warm her fingers? She pulled one out. "Ritsch!" How it spluttered, how it blazed! It burnt with a bright clear flame, just like a little candle when she held her hand round it. It was a very curious candle, too. The little girl fancied that she was sitting in front of a big stove with polished brass feet and handles. There was a splendid fire blazing in it and warming her so beautifully, but—what happened? Just as she was stretching out her feet to warm them, the blaze went out, the stove vanished, and she was left sitting with the end of the burnt-out match in her hand. She struck a new one, it burnt, it blazed up, and where the light fell upon the wall against which she lay, it became transparent like gauze, and she could see right through it into the room inside. There was a table spread with a snowy cloth and pretty china; a roast goose stuffed with apples and prunes was steaming on it. And what was even better, the goose hopped from the dish with the carving knife and fork sticking in his back, and it waddled across the floor. It came right up to the poor child, and then—the match went out and there was nothing to be seen but the thick black wall.

She lit another match. This time she was sitting under a lovely Christmas tree. It was much bigger and more beautifully decorated than the one she had seen when she had peeped through the glass doors at the rich merchant's house this Christmas day. Thousands of lighted candles gleamed upon its branches, and coloured pictures such as she had seen in the shop windows looked down upon her. The little girl stretched out both her hands towards them— then out went the match. All the Christmas candles rose higher and higher, till she saw that they were only the twinkling stars. One of them fell and made a bright streak of light across the sky. "Some one is dying," thought the little girl; for her old grandmother, the only person who had ever been kind to her, used to say, "When a star falls a soul is going up to God."

Now she struck another match against the wall, and this time it was her grandmother who appeared in the circle of flame. She saw her quite clearly and distinctly, looking so gentle and happy.

"Grandmother!" cried the little creature. "Oh, do take me with you! I know you will vanish when the match goes out; you will vanish like the warm stove, the delicious goose, and the beautiful Christmas tree!"

She hastily struck a whole bundle of matches, because she did so want to keep her grandmother with her. The light of the matches made it as bright as day. Grandmother had never before looked so big or so beautiful. She lifted the little girl up in her arms, and they soared in a halo of light and joy, far, far above the earth, where there was no more cold, no hunger, no pain, for they were with God.

In the cold morning light the poor little girl sat there, in the corner between the houses, with rosy cheeks and a smile on her face—dead. Frozen to death on the last night of the Old Year. New Year's day revealed the little body still sitting with the ends of the burnt-out matches in her hand. She must have tried to warm herself, they said. Nobody knew what beautiful visions she had seen, nor in what a halo she had entered with her grandmother upon the glories of the New Year!

Christmas at the Hollow Tree Inn

Uncle Toby Told the Children This Story One Christmas Eve. It Was Snowing Outside and They Were Wondering How It Was in the Far Deep Woods

By ALBERT BIGELOW PAINE

ONCE upon a time, when the Robin, and Turtle, and Squirrel, and Jack Rabbit had all gone home for the winter, nobody was left in the Hollow Tree except the 'Coon and 'Possum and the old black Crow. Of course the others used to come back and visit them pretty often, and Mr. Dog, too, now that he had got to be good friends with all the Deep Woods people, and they thought a good deal of him when they got to know him better. Mr. Dog told them a lot of things they had never heard of before, things that he'd learned at Mr. Man's house, and maybe that's one reason why they got to liking him so well.

He told them about Santa Claus, for one thing, and how the old fellow came down the chimney on Christmas Eve to bring presents to Mr. Man and his children, who always hung up their stockings for them, and Mr. Dog said that once he had hung up his stocking, too, and got a nice bone in it, that was so good he had buried and dug it up again as much as six times before spring. He said that Santa Claus always came to Mr. Man's house, and that whenever the children hung up their stockings they were always sure to get something in them.

Well, the Hollow Tree people had never heard of Santa Claus. They knew about Christmas, of course, because everybody, even the cows and sheep, know about that; but they had never heard of Santa Claus. You see, Santa Claus only comes to Mr. Man's house, but they didn't know that, either, so they thought if they just hung up their stockings he'd come there, too, and that's what they made up their minds to do. They talked about it a great deal together, and Mr. 'Possum looked over all his stockings to pick out the biggest one he had, and Mr. Crow he made himself a new pair on purpose. Mr. 'Coon said he never knew Mr. Crow to make himself such big stockings before, but Mr. Crow said he was getting old and needed things bigger, and when he loaned one of his new stockings to Mr. 'Coon, Mr. 'Coon said, "That's so," and that he guessed they were about right, after all. They didn't tell anybody about it at first, but by and by they told Mr. Dog what they were going to do, and when Mr. Dog heard it he wanted to laugh right out. You see, he knew Santa Claus never went anywhere except to Mr. Man's house, and he thought it would be a great joke on the Hollow Tree people when they hung up their stockings and didn't get anything.

But by and by Mr. Dog thought about something else. He thought it would be too bad, too, for them to be disappointed that way. You see, Mr. Dog liked them all now, and when he had thought about that a minute he made up his mind to do something. And this is what it was—he made up his mind to play Santa Claus!

Well, he had to work pretty hard, I tell you, to get things ready. It wasn't so hard to get the presents as it was to rig up his Santa Claus dress. He found some long wool out in Mr. Man's barn for his white whiskers, and he put some that wasn't so long on the edges of his overcoat and boot tops and around an old hat he had. Then he borrowed a big sack he found out there, too, and fixed it up to swing over his back just as he had seen Santa Claus do in the pictures. He had a lot of nice things to take along. Three tender young chickens he'd borrowed from Mr. Man, for one thing, and then he bought some new neckties for the Hollow Tree folks all around, and a big, striped candy cane for each one, because candy canes always looked well sticking out of a stocking. Besides all that, he had a new pipe for each, and a package of tobacco. You see, Mr. Dog lived with Mr. Man, and didn't ever have to buy much for himself, so he had always saved his money. He had even more things than that, but I can't remember just now what they were; and when he started out all dressed up like Santa Claus, I tell you his bag was pretty heavy, and he almost wished before he got there that he hadn't started with quite so much.

It got heavier and heavier all the way, and he was glad enough to get there. He set his bag down to rest a minute before climbing the stairs, and then opened the doors softly and listened. He didn't hear a thing except Mr. Crow and Mr. 'Coon and Mr. 'Possum breathing pretty low, and he knew they might wake up any minute, and he wouldn't have been caught there in the midst of things for a good deal. So he slipped up just as easy as anything, and when he got up in the big parlor room he almost had

to laugh right out loud, for there were the stockings sure enough, all hung up in a row, and a card with a name on it over each one telling who it belonged to.

Then he listened again, and all at once he jumped and held his breath, for he heard Mr. 'Possum say something. But Mr. 'Possum was only talking in his sleep, and saying, "I'll take another piece, please," and Mr. Dog knew he was dreaming about the mince pie he'd had for supper.

So then he opened his bag and filled the stockings. He put in mixed candy and nuts and little things first, and then the pipes and tobacco and candy canes, so they'd show at the top, and hung a nice dressed chicken outside. I tell you they looked fine! It almost made Mr. Dog wish he had a stocking of his own there to fill, and he forgot all about them waking up, and sat down in a chair to look at the stockings. It was a nice rocking-chair, and over in a dark corner where they wouldn't be apt to see him, even if one of them did wake up and stick his head out of his room, so Mr. Dog felt pretty safe now, anyway. He rocked softly, and looked and looked at the nice stockings, and thought how pleased they'd be in the morning, and how tired he was. You've heard about people being as tired as a dog; and that's just how Mr. Dog felt. He was so tired he didn't feel a bit like starting home, and by and by—he never did know how it happened—but by and by Mr. Dog went sound asleep right there in his chair, with all his Santa Claus clothes on.

And there he sat, with his empty bag in his hand and the nice full stockings in front of him, all night long. Even when it came morning and began to get light Mr. Dog didn't know it; he just slept right on, he was that tired. Then pretty soon the door of Mr. 'Possum's room opened and he poked out his head. And just then the door of Mr. 'Coon's room opened and he poked out his head. Then the door of the old black Crow's opened and out poked his head. They all looked toward the stockings, and they didn't see Mr. Dog, or even each other, at all. They saw their stockings, though, and Mr. 'Coon said all at once:

"Oh, there's something in my stocking!"

And then Mr. Crow says, "Oh, there's something in my stocking, too!"

And Mr. 'Possum says, "Oh, there's something in all our stockings!"

And with that they gave a great hurrah all together, and rushed out and grabbed their stockings and turned around just in time to see Mr. Dog jump right straight up out of his chair, for he did not know where he was the least bit in the world.

"Oh, there's Santa Claus himself!" they all shouted together, and made a rush for their rooms, for they were scared almost to death. But it all dawned on Mr. Dog in a second, and he commenced to laugh and hurrah to think what a joke it was on everybody. And when they heard Mr. Dog laugh they knew him right away, and they all came up and looked at him, and he had to tell just what he'd done and everything; so they emptied out their stockings on the floor and ate some of the presents and looked at the others, until they almost forgot about breakfast, just as children do on Christmas morning.

Then Mr. Crow said, all at once, that he'd make a little coffee, and that Mr. Dog must stay and have some, and by and by they made him promise to spend the day with them and be there when the Robin and the Squirrel and Mr. Turtle and Jack Rabbit came for Christmas dinner, which he did.

And it was snowing hard outside, which made it a nicer Christmas than if it hadn't been, and when all the others came they brought presents, too. And when they saw Mr. Dog dressed up as Santa Claus and heard how he'd gone to sleep and been caught, they laughed and laughed. And it snowed so hard that they had to stay all night, and after dinner they sat around the fire and told stories. And they had to stay the next night, too, and all that Christmas week. It was the very nicest Christmas that ever was in the Hollow Tree, or in the Big Deep Woods anywhere.

9

Everyone Will Agree With Uncle Toby that No
Child's Christmas Could Be Complete Without
These Two Old Nursery Favorites, Read Aloud
Before the Stockings Are Mysteriously Filled.

Jest 'Fore Christmas

By Eugene Field

Father calls me William, sister calls me Will,
Mother calls me Willie, but the fellers call me Bill!
Mighty glad I ain't a girl—ruther be a boy,
Without them sashes, curls, an' things that's worn by Fauntleroy!
Love to chawnk green apples an' go swimmin' in the lake—
Hate to take the caster-ile they give for belly-ache!
'Most all the time, the whole year round, there ain't no flies on me,
But jest 'fore Christmas I'm as good as I kin be!

Got a yeller dog named Sport, sick him on the cat;
First thing she knows she doesn't know where she is at!
Got a clipper sled, an' when us kids goes out to slide,
'Long comes a grocery cart, an' we all hook a ride!
But sometimes when the grocery man is worrited an' cross,
He reaches at us with his whip, an' larrups up his hoss,
An' then I laff an' holler, "Oh, ye never teched *me*!"
But jest 'fore Christmas I'm as good as I kin be!

Gran'ma says she hopes that when I git to be a man
I'll be a missionarer like her oldest brother, Dan,
As was et up by the cannibuls that lived in Ceylon's Isle,
Where every prospeck pleases, an' only man is vile!
But gran'ma she has never been to see a Wild West show,
Nor read the Life of Daniel Boone, or else I guess she'd know
That Buff'lo Bill and cowboys is good enough for me!
Excep' jest 'fore Christmas, when I'm good as I kin be!

And then old Sport he hangs around, so solemn-like an' still,
His eyes they keep a-sayin': "What's the matter, little Bill?"
The old cat sneaks down off her perch an' wonders what's become
Of them two enemies of hern that used to make things hum!

But I am so perlite an' 'tend so earnestly to biz,
That mother says to father: "How improved our Willie is!"
But father, havin' been a boy hisself, suspicions me
When just 'fore Christmas, I'm as good as I kin be!

For Christmas, with its lots an' lots of candies, cakes an' toys,
Was made, they say, for proper kids an' not for naughty boys;
So wash yer face an' bresh yer hair, an' mind yer p's an' q's,
An' don't bust out yer pantaloons, an' don't wear out yer shoes;
Say "Yessum" to the ladies, an' "Yessur" to the men,
An' when they's company, don't pass yer plate for pie again;
But, thinking of the things yer'd like to see upon that tree,
Jest 'fore Christmas be as good as yer kin be!

A Visit from St. Nicholas

By CLEMENT C. MOORE

'Twas the night before Christmas, when all through the house
Not a creature was stirring, not even a mouse;
The stockings were hung by the chimney with care,
In hopes that St. Nicholas soon would be there;
The children were nestled all snug in their beds,
While visions of sugar-plums danced in their heads;
And Mamma in her kerchief, and I in my cap,
Had just settled our brains for a long winter's nap—
When out on the lawn there rose such a clatter,
I sprang from my bed to see what was the matter.
Away to the window I flew like a flash,
Tore open the shutters and threw up the sash.
  The moon, on the breast of the new-fallen snow,
Gave a luster of mid-day to objects below;
When, what to my wondering eyes should appear,
But a miniature sleigh, and eight tiny reindeer,
With a little old driver, so lively and quick,
I knew in a moment it must be St. Nick.
More rapid than eagles his coursers they came,
And he whistled, and shouted, and called them by name;
"Now, Dasher! now, Dancer! now, Prancer and Vixen!
On! Comet, on! Cupid, on! Dunder and Blitzen—
To the top of the porch, to the top of the wall!
Now, dash away, dash away, dash away all!"
As dry leaves that before the wild hurricane fly,
When they meet with an obstacle, mount to the sky,
So, up to the house-top the coursers they flew,
With a sleigh full of toys—and St. Nicholas too.
And then in a twinkling I heard on the roof,
The prancing and pawing of each little hoof.

As I drew in my head, and was turning around,
Down the chimney St. Nicholas came with a bound.
He was dressed all in fur from his head to his foot,
And his clothes were all tarnished with ashes and soot;
A bundle of toys he had flung on his back,
And he looked like a peddler just opening his pack.
His eyes how they twinkled! his dimples how merry!
His cheeks were like roses, his nose like a cherry;
His droll little mouth was drawn up like a bow,
And the beard on his chin was as white as the snow;
The stump of a pipe he held tight in his teeth,

And the smoke, it encircled his head like a wreath.
He had a broad face, and a little round belly,
That shook when he laughed, like a bowl full of jelly.
He was chubby and plump—a right jolly old elf;
And I laughed when I saw him, in spite of myself.
A wink of his eye, and a twist of his head,
Soon gave me to know I had nothing to dread.
He spoke not a word, but went straight to his work,
And filled all the stockings; then turned with a jerk,
And laying his finger aside of his nose,
And giving a nod, up the chimney he rose.

He sprang to his sleigh, to his team gave a whistle,
And away they all flew like the down of a thistle;
But I heard him exclaim, ere he drove out of sight,
"HAPPY CHRISTMAS TO ALL, AND TO ALL A GOOD-
    NIGHT!"

10

Good Christmas Plays for Children Are Rare, but Uncle Toby Has Found Two Which Are Sure to Bring Delight to Youthful Hearts.

Alias Santa Claus

By Percival Wilde*

It is Christmas Day in the Millman home, and the large room upon which our curtain rises is appropriately adorned for the occasion. The lighting fixtures are gaily festooned. A holly wreath hangs at the big windows at the back; more wreaths hang from the doors at either side. There is a wealth of hothouse flowers.

Near the center is a very large and magnificently trimmed Christmas tree; a tree so splendid that you gasp when you see it. It is surrounded by a small ocean of gifts; enough to stock a fair-sized store. A gorgeous bicycle has a place of honor; it is hemmed in by a whole library of books, a pair of boxing-gloves, two sleds, a regiment of the very latest mechanical wonders, enough musical instruments to equip a miniature band, and any number of games. There is everything you can think of—and more.

The toys are most expensive, and you wonder how many children are to be made happy by them—and then we tell you that they are all for the exclusive use of David Millman, Jr., who is seven years old, and who would greatly prefer permission to put on rompers and play on some not too clean floor. But being an only child of a widowed father, and being heir to a string of banks, and at least one railroad, and half a dozen mansions in town and country, he is not permitted to do such things.

As our play begins the room is empty—but not for long. A face peers in through the window at the back, the sash is raised slowly and noiselessly, and a fourteen-year-old boy hoists himself across the sill. He is roughly dressed. His eyes are covered by a black mask with slits in it. Under his arm, with exaggerated care, he carries a gaily decorated box of candy.

He looks about stealthily, tiptoeing about the room. Then he turns to the window to hiss to an accomplice:

* Printed by special arrangement with the author and D. Appleton-Century Co.

SLIM—Coast's clear! (BILL, *another boy, masked, and wearing a badly fitting beard and whiskers, climbs into the room. His appearance is one-half villainous, one-half pathetic. He is thin, and he is suffering from a cold.*) Shh!

BILL—I ain't makin' no noise—not a w'isper. (*He upsets a chair. It is loaded with mechanical toys, and falls with a fearful racket.*)

SLIM—Sufferin' cats! (*They rush to concealment. There is a dreadful pause. Presently they poke their heads out cautiously.*)

BILL—Nobody hoid it.

SLIM—Dey must be deef in dis house. (*He steals to one door and applies his ear to the keyhole. BILL, timid in the presence of so much luxury, moves to the other.*) Well?

BILL—Naw—not a sound.

SLIM—Deef—or asleep!

BILL—Slim, pipe de tree!

SLIM—Ain't it a boid?

BILL—It's a humdinger! It's a pippin! It's a looloo! (*He surveys it from top to bottom.*) T'ink of it, Slim, just t'ink of it: a tree like dat—an' fer *one* kid!

SLIM—Pretty soft, I'll tell de woild!

BILL—'Tain't fair! 'Tain't! Here we got eight young uns at home an' I promised 'em a tree fer Christmas, an' dey ain't got nuttin': not even a geranium! Gee, wouldn't dey love dis!

SLIM (*scornfully*)—Are yuh gettin' mushy?

BILL (*with pathetic bravado*)—*Me* mushy? I'm hard-boiled! (*Suddenly*) Say ——

SLIM—W'at?

BILL—I gotta sneeze.

SLIM—Sneeze, an' I'll moider yuh! (*He crosses hastily to BILL, and waves his arms grotesquely in a futile effort to prevent him from sneezing.*) Now! . . . Now! . . . Now! . . .

BILL (*thunderously*)—A-choo! (SLIM *hastens to hide; BILL follows. There is another dreadful pause, but nobody comes to disturb them. Presently BILL becomes visible again.*) Nobody hoid.

SLIM (*with unlimited sarcasm*)—Dey t'ought it was just blastin' in de subway!

BILL—Wouldn't be surprized if dey did. Sounded like it.

SLIM—Now keep yer eyes open! (*He crosses stealthily to the tree, and deposits his box of candy at its foot. It is a large box tied up with red ribbon. It is very conspicuous.*) Dere!

BILL—Yer sure it ain't gonna hoit de kid, Slim?

SLIM—Leave it to me!

BILL (*hopefully*)—Maybe he won't eat it.

SLIM—W'at kid won't eat candy?

BILL—Dis one's a millionaire kid.

SLIM—He's a kid just de same, ain't he? He'll eat one—maybe two. W'at's de diff? One'll do de trick fine an' dandy. It won't hoit him none——

BILL—How do yuh know?

SLIM—Knock-out drops, dat's all dere's in 'em. He'll go off to sleep just as nice an' easy——

BILL—W'at good's dat gonna do us? De rest of 'em ain't gonna go to sleep, an' dere's a noice, an' dere's a guard dat watches him every minute, an' dere's——

SLIM (*interrupting*)—Dey'll all holler fer help—see? Dey'll run fer a doctor. Dey'll leave him right here, alone, an' dead to de woild, an' den we lift him outa de winder, wit'out nobody to stop us. (*He rubs his hands happily.*) We'll get a million—a cool million—outa his dad before we give him back.

BILL (*eagerly*)—Do yuh t'ink he'll pay it?

SLIM (*grimly*)—He'll pay it if he expec's to lay eyes on dat kid again.

BILL (*anxiously*)—Slim, yuh wouldn't hoit de kid?

SLIM—I don't know what I'd do. I'm desprit! (*He surveys* BILL *with scorn.*) Are yuh gettin' mushy again?

BILL (*with his same pathetic bravado*)—Me mushy? I'm hard-boiled!

SLIM—Well, stay dat way! (*He leads the way toward the window.*) Stick to me, Bill, an' in a week we'll be rollin' in money! A million! A million!

BILL—I don't need dat much.

SLIM (*going out at the window*)—I'll take w'at yuh don't want.

BILL (*following*)—I gotta sneeze! (SLIM'S *arm reaches up, grabs him by the collar, and hauls him out head first. The window closes.*)

SLIM (*outside*)—Now! . . . Now! . . . Now! . . . (*There is a monstrous sneeze.*)

> (*There is only an instant's pause this time. Then, from the right, enters* HALLIGAN, *a brawny middle-aged Irishman, whose business it is to guard the young millionaire. He is followed by* VICKY, *the nurse.*)

HALLIGAN—I thought I was after hearin' something.

VICKY—You're forever hearing things, Mr. Halligan!

HALLIGAN (*seriously*)—I'm paid to keep my eyes and ears open. I'm on the job. (*He looks about the room, goes to the window and looks out.*)

VICKY (*impressed by his earnestness*)—See anybody?

HALLIGAN—Nary a soul!

VICKY—I'm glad of that! With a young millionaire to look out for, it's nerve-racking, I tell you! You never know what to expect —you never know what might happen.

DAVID (*saunters in at the right. He is a winsome, appealing boy of seven, dressed in a most expensive and most uncomfortable manner. There is an eager look in his face—a look of yearning that has never been gratified. What he wants he cannot have, and what he has means very little indeed to him*)—Hello, Vicky.

VICKY—Master David, you knew you weren't to come in here until ten o'clock.

DAVID (*glancing at a wrist-watch*)—It's nearly that now, Vicky.

VICKY—Exactly ten, your father said: ten exactly. He's very busy dictating letters in his study—he's brought a lot of work home from the office—but he's going to give you a few minutes.

DAVID (*without sentimentality*)—I know what that means: a few minutes.

VICKY—You're not to look at the Christmas tree until he comes.

DAVID—All right; I won't look. (*He turns his back squarely on the tree.*) I'll watch the door, and wait. (*He faces the left-hand door.*)

VICKY (*sotto voce, to* HALLIGAN)—Did you ever see such a child? You'd think he couldn't help looking.

HALLIGAN—He doesn't care about the tree.

VICKY (*snapping her fingers*)—Not that much!

HALLIGAN—He doesn't want to see his presents. It's his father he's after wantin', I think. Just that.

VICKY—Shh!

> (*A clock strikes ten.* DAVID *glances nervously at his watch.* HALLIGAN *stiffens to attention.* VICKY *stands erect, expectantly. The door at the left opens, and* MILLMAN, *a fine-looking man in his forties, enters briskly, snapping shut his watch as he crosses the threshold. He is all alertness and no waste motion—his time is precious—he never forgets that.*)

MILLMAN—Merry Christmas, Davy.

DAVID (*whose lips are trembling and whose eyes never leave his father*)—Merry Christmas, Daddy.

MILLMAN (*turning to the others, and handing each an envelope*) —Merry Christmas. Merry Christmas.

HALLIGAN—Thank you, sir—and the same to you.

VICKY—Merry Christmas—and thank you.

MILLMAN—Tut-tut! (*He turns briskly toward the tree.*) Well, Davy, and how do you like your tree?

DAVID (*not glancing at it*)—Very much, Daddy.

MILLMAN—It was nice of Santa to bring you so many presents.

DAVID—Very nice, Daddy.

MILLMAN (*examining cards*)—And here are more presents from your little friends—and your uncle Joe—and your uncle Elbridge —and your uncle Twombley ——

DAVID—Yes, Daddy.

MILLMAN (*examining an envelope*)—Here's an envelop from your aunt Mary—and look what's in it! (*He draws out a yellow-backed bill.*)

DAVID—You take care of it for me, Daddy.

MILLMAN (*putting the envelope in his pocket*)—Here's an electric train from Santa. Switches, and stations, and coal-cars—I declare, it's a wonderful train. Isn't it, Halligan?

HALLIGAN—It is that, sir.

MILLMAN—You ought to be a very happy boy, Davy.

DAVID—Yes, Daddy.

MILLMAN (*glancing at his watch again*)—I must go now. You don't mind, do you, Davy? Important cablegrams—letters ——

DAVID—I understand, Daddy.

MILLMAN (*already in the doorway*)—By the way, there's a present from me downstairs—a new limousine. Later on you'll go riding in it.

DAVID (*rushing to him with sudden, pathetic eagerness*)—Will you come too, Daddy?

MILLMAN—Sorry, Davy—haven't time. (*He pats the boy's head and nods pleasantly to the others.*) Good morning. (*The door closes behind him, and* DAVID, *as if struck by a blow, withdraws again into his shell.*)

VICKY—A fine gentleman, Mr. Millman!

HALLIGAN—That he is!

VICKY—Did you see the check he gave me? (*Shows it.*)

HALLIGAN—Just take a look at this one!

VICKY (*fervently*)—The salt of the earth!

HALLIGAN—A fine gentleman!

DAVID (*who has been motionless, now turns to* HALLIGAN, *in joyous assent*)—A fine gentleman, isn't he, Halligan? (*Proudly.*) When my father walks along the street everybody stops to look at him! I can see the people nudging each other, and saying, "There goes Mr. Millman." And the newspapers send men here to take his picture—but father's too busy to let them do that. And when I go out I hear everybody say, "There goes Millman's boy." And all the policemen touch their caps and talk to me.

HALLIGAN—Yes, I've seen that many a time.

DAVID—And it's all because daddy's such a fine man!

HALLIGAN (*finding the statement difficult to correct*)—Yes; I guess that's the reason. (*He is in distress.*)

VICKY (*coming to the rescue*)—Now you may look at the tree, Master David.

DAVID (*suddenly unenthusiastic, barely glancing at the tree*)—It's very nice.

VICKY—Is that all you can say about it?

DAVID—It's just as nice as the one we had last year—and that was the nicest I ever saw.

VICKY (*taking up the gifts*)—Boxing-gloves!

DAVID (*tentatively, knowing what to expect*)—May I put them on?

VICKY—Some day, perhaps—not just yet. Sleds!

DAVID—May I go coasting on them?

VICKY—Next year, maybe—not now. A trumpet!

DAVID—May I blow on it?

VICKY—Mercy, no! Not until it has been boiled.

DAVID—But that'll spoil the paint.

VICKY—Better to spoil the paint than to ruin your health.

DAVID (*disappointed*)—Oh, all right.

HALLIGAN (*coming to the rescue in his turn*)—I have a list of the presents here. (*He produces a long sheet.*) Two railroad trains —complete.

DAVID (*not boasting; simply stating facts*)—I have four already.

HALLIGAN—Two phonographs.

DAVID—I have three—and I can't play more than one at once.

HALLIGAN—Your cousin Willy sent you a set of books.

DAVID—And what did I send him?

HALLIGAN (*referring to the list*)—You sent him a Boy Scout outfit.

DAVID—Why didn't he keep the books and send me the outfit?

HALLIGAN (*avoiding the question*)—Your aunt Genevieve sent you a bicycle.

DAVID (*interested despite himself*)—Oh, that's nice! (*He moves toward it.*)

VICKY (*interposing*)—You may ride on it when you're older.

DAVID—But not now?

VICKY (*with real solicitude*)—You might hurt yourself, Master David.

DAVID (*crestfallen; turning to* HALLIGAN)—Don't read me any more, Halligan. (*Christmas is a complete failure so far as he is concerned, but the child in him is irrepressible. He examines some of the gifts.* VICKY *helps.*)

VICKY—A tennis racket.

DAVID—That'll be fun this summer!

HALLIGAN—It will that!

DAVID—I may play with it?

VICKY—All you like.

DAVID—Good! Watch my overhand! (*He swings the racket.*)

VICKY (*taking it from him*)—Not in the house, Master David; you'll break something.

DAVID—I knew there was a string tied to it.

VICKY (*indicating*)—Golf clubs.

DAVID—For the summer?

VICKY—Naturally for the summer.

DAVID (*nodding*)—I see; it's winter now. (*He sees a pair of ice skates, and takes them up.*) Do these have to wait for the summer, too?

HALLIGAN (*impressively*)—You're to go to the rink with them this afternoon.

DAVID—That *will* be nice!

VICKY—They're a gift from us, Master David ——

HALLIGAN—From me and her.

DAVID (*sincerely*)—Thank you, Vicky. (*He kisses her.*) Thanks, Halligan. (*He shakes hands.*) You couldn't have given me anything I'd like better. (*He feels the edge.*) They're sharp, aren't they?

HALLIGAN—I saw to that.

VICKY (*alarmed*)—Be careful, Master David!

DAVID (*smiling*)—You aren't going to get them away from me! (*He gives them to* HALLIGAN, *and turns back to the tree.*) Look!

HALLIGAN (*following his glance*)—Candy!

VICKY (*horrified*)—Candy! Who sent it?

HALLIGAN—It's not down on the list.

VICKY (*kneeling to examine it*)—There's no card.

DAVID—I guess it came from Santa Claus.

VICKY (*reluctantly*)—Of course you mayn't eat it.

DAVID—That's all right, Vicky; I don't mind.

VICKY (*who has opened the box*)—There's no card inside, but it looks lovely.

DAVID—I mayn't have any, Vicky; eat it yourself.

VICKY—Do you really want me to?

DAVID—Of course, Vicky.

VICKY (*eating and smacking her lips*)—They're good! Have one, Mr. Halligan?

HALLIGAN—I don't mind if I do. (*He eats a candy.*)

DAVID (*watching with interest*)—What do they taste like?

VICKY—Chocolate —— (*Takes another.*)

HALLIGAN—With strawberry cream inside —— (*Taking another.*)

VICKY—This one has a cherry.

HALLIGAN—This has a walnut.

DAVID—Santa Claus makes good candy, doesn't he? Some day, when I'm older, he'll make some that I can eat. I'd like that!

VICKY—Another, Mr. Halligan?

HALLIGAN (*swallowing hard and passing his hand over his forehead*)—No, thanks.

VICKY—(*rising suddenly and tottering*)—Mr. Halligan—I don't feel well. Please get me some water.

HALLIGAN (*alarmed; hastening out of the room*)—Right away!

DAVID—What's the matter, Vicky? Vicky, dear?

VICKY—It's nothing, Master David. It'll pass away in a minute. (*She sways, and* DAVID *steadies her.*) I feel dizzy—very dizzy—all of a sudden.

DAVID—Sit down, Vicky.

VICKY (*catching the back of a chair*)—I can't imagine what's wrong. Nothing like this has ever happened to me before. Oh dear! Why doesn't Halligan bring the water? Why doesn't he bring it? I'm so dizzy—so dizzy. (*From the hall at the right there is the sound of a heavy fall, accompanied by the crash of breaking glass.*)

DAVID (*alarmed*)—Halligan fell!

VICKY (*reeling toward the door*)—Mr. Halligan! Mr. Halligan! I'm afraid I'm going to faint. (*On the threshold a sudden suspicion comes to her, and she pulls herself together with a heroic effort.*) David, Davy, boy! Don't touch the candy! (*She collapses on the threshold.*)

DAVID (*on his knees at her side*)—Vicky! Vicky, dear! Answer me, Vicky! (*During the last few seconds the window has been raised, and SLIM has come into the room.*)

SLIM (*to BILL, who follows*)—It woiked.

BILL—De kid didn't eat de candy.

SLIM—De udders did—dat suits me.

DAVID (*rising to confront the newcomers*)—What are you doing here?

BILL (*pushing SLIM to one side easily*)—Nuttin' to get excited about, kid; yer lady friend's all right—see? (*He leads DAVID back into the room; SLIM thrusts the door shut, and locks it.*) She's just day-dreamin'—takin' a little cat nap. It won't hoit her a bit—honest! She'll feel fine when she wakes up.

DAVID—What happened to Halligan?

BILL—He's day-dreamin', too. De two of 'em are day-dreamin' togedder—nice an' sociable-like—see? Dey're dreamin' about de little boidies singin' in de tree tops. Ain't dat pretty? (*SLIM has come forward. BILL waves a hand.*) Meet my friend Slim.

DAVID (*extending a hand*)—How do you do?

SLIM (*shaking hands*)—Pleased to meet-cha.

BILL—Slim an' me—we're gonna look after yuh fer a w'ile.

DAVID—Yes? (*He looks up at BILL with sudden recognition.*) You don't have to tell me who *you* are!

BILL (*worried*)—I don't?

DAVID—I've seen you before!

BILL—Yuh know my name?

DAVID—Of course! Who doesn't? (*He pauses while* BILL *plainly shows his anxiety.*) Why, you're Santa Claus!

SLIM (*overcome and relieved*)—W'at? W'at did yuh say?

DAVID (*laughing*)—You're Santa Claus and you know you are!

SLIM—Ha! Ha! (*He breaks into guffaws.*)

BILL (*poking* SLIM *violently in the midriff with his elbow*)—Yuh guessed it right de very foist time, kid. John W. Santa—dat's me! (*He tidies his impossible beard and whiskers.*)

DAVID—I knew you right off!

BILL—Yuh sure did!

DAVID (*intensely interested, catching his hand*)—Did you have a cold trip coming here?

BILL—W'at's dat?

DAVID—Wasn't it cold, coming all the way from the North Pole?

BILL—Well, it wasn't so bad after we got to a Hunner an' Twenty-fift' Street ——

DAVID (*fascinated*)—No?

BILL—Den de goin' was pretty good.

DAVID—But before you got there?

BILL—It *was* a wee bit chilly.

SLIM—It was sixty below.

DAVID—Sixty below what?

BILL—Not below nuttin'. Just below—see? (*He gesticulates vividly, placing his hand parallel to the floor at the level of his ankles.*) Dat was w'ere I caught cold. I gotta sneeze.

SLIM—Now! . . . Now! . . . Now! . . .

DAVID—Oh, let him sneeze! (BILL *sneezes.*) God bless you!

BILL—Much obliged.

DAVID—That's all right. I always say "God bless you" when anybody sneezes.

SLIM (*returning to the main topic*)—We're gonna take care of yuh—me an' Bill.

BILL—We're gonna take yuh fer a long ride.

DAVID—Are we going to the North Pole?

BILL—Foider den dat. (*Approaching him.*) But you gotta keep quiet!

DAVID (*with a nod of comprehension*)—I know; you don't want to frighten the reindeer.

SLIM (*alarmed*)—De w'ich?

DAVID—Blixen and Vixen ——

BILL—W'at?

DAVID—and Prancer and Dancer ——

SLIM (*decidedly worried, to* BILL)—Did youse see any of dem guys w'en yuh come in?

BILL—Maybe dey was under cover. (*To* DAVID.)—Say, kid, w'ere do dey keep?

DAVID (*puzzled*)—Keep?

BILL—W'ere do dey hang out? W'ere do dey park? W'ere's deir stampin'-ground?

DAVID—Oh, outside!

BILL (*to* SLIM)—I told yuh de house was watched!

DAVID (*quoting some book*)—"Drawing Santa Claus from his home in the North, reindeer, swifter than the wind, swift as light ——"

SLIM (*beginning to understand*)—Hey! I get him now! He's talkin' about a noo kind of flivver!

DAVID—"Swifter even than dreams, sturdy and strong, champing at their bits, sparks coming from their nostrils ——"

BILL (*nodding*)—De kid's got de right dope, Slim. (*To* DAVID.) Dey're waitin' fer us outside: balloon tires, an' four-w'eel brakes, an' sparks just w'ere yuh said. Come on.

DAVID (*going toward the window*)—They're in a big hurry, aren't they? They know we're coming, Santa Claus. I hear them shaking their sleigh-bells. (*Sleigh-bells are audible.*)

BILL (*much alarmed*)—Do yuh hear dat, Slim?

DAVID (*with glee*)—Sleigh-bells!

SLIM—Shh! (*They hide in corners of the room.* DAVID *cannot understand their actions; he looks about, puzzled. Then a ten-*

year-old girl, wearing a harness covered with sleigh-bells, appears at the window.)

BESSIE (*softly*)—Bill! (*More loudly.*) Bill! Bill! (*She spies* DAVID.) Is he here? (DAVID *nods silently, and indicates with his thumb where* BILL *is hiding.* BESSIE *climbs into the room, bells jangling.*) Bill, we found yuh! (*Climbing through the window come seven more children, in decreasing sizes. The smaller ones are helped by the larger, and the smallest, which is but an infant, is carried by one of the others. They are all badly dressed. Their clothes are torn and shabby; their stockings are full of holes; and they average about three-quarters of a glove to every hand. But they are all extraordinarily happy, and not at all shy about showing it. And being* BILL'S *younger brothers and sisters, they are as tough as the proverbial nails.*)

A BABBLE OF TALK—Hey, give us a hand, Pete! Look out! Yuh'll fall! Mind de baby! Gimme a good push! Up yuh go!

BILL (*emerging from his concealment, looking decidedly sheepish*)—How did youse get here?

BESSIE—We seen yuh go, an' we run after yuh.

BILL—All of youse?

BESSIE (*nodding*)—Maggie carried de baby.

MAGGIE—See brudder's funny face, baby?

SLIM (*coming out, and speaking with boundless contempt*)— Dat's de last time I ask a family man to tackle a job along wit' me!

BESSIE—Bill, yuh promised us a Christmas tree!

PETE—An' we knowed yuh'd get us one!

ANNIE—Yuh said yuh was gonna get one, didn't yuh, Bill?

MAGGIE—So we followed yuh all de way ——

T'EODORE—An' here it is!

> (*There is a chorus of delighted screams as the children surround the tree.*)

BESSIE—Bill, what a peach of a tree!

PETE—Some tree!

ANNIE—Lookit de presents!

T'EODORE—Golly, lookit de presents!

MAGGIE—See de boo'ful tree, baby? (*She makes the baby clap its hands.*)

DAVID (*puzzled, as the children, shrilling their delight, descend upon the gifts*)—Say, Santa Claus, I didn't know you had a family.

SLIM (*with infinite disgust*)—Kid, you said a mout'ful!

DAVID—Are they all related to you?

BILL (*not too modestly*)—Me eight brudders an' sisters—count 'em. Bessie—an' Pete—dey're twins. An' Maggie—dat's her holdin' de baby—an' T'eodore—an' Annie—an' Grover—an' Woodrow—an' Calvin—dat's de baby.

DAVID—Do they all come from the North Pole?

BESSIE (*with injured American pride*)—W'at do yuh t'ink? We're a lot of Polanders?

BILL—De Nort' Pole? De Nort' Pole's warm next to w'ere dey come from. My paw ain't woikin'—an' de landlord toined off de heat w'en I didn't pay de rent.

DAVID—Rent? What's rent?

SLIM (*as BILL gazes appealingly at him*)—Yuh started dis. Yuh tell him.

BILL—Rent? Rent's somethin' yuh pay w'en yuh get money.

DAVID—And when you don't get it?

BILL—Yuh don't.

SLIM (*becoming impatient*)—Say, w'at I wanna know is dis: is dis a kidnappin' party, or is dis a kid party?

DAVID—What's a kidnapping party, Santa Claus?

BILL—I'll show yuh. (*He calls to the children.*)—Hey, fellers, we're gonna beat it.

PETE—Naw!

BESSIE—We don't wanna go, Bill.

ANNIE—We wanna play wit' de presents!

T'EODORE—Lookit de sleds!

PETE—An' de boxin'-gloves!

ANNIE—An' de railroad trains!

BESSIE—An' de trumpets!

MAGGIE—See de pretty flowers, baby?

PETE (*parceling out the musical instruments*)—Yuh take dis—an' yuh take dis—an' yuh take dis—an' w'en I say ready, yuh all blow to onct!

SLIM (*anxiously*)—Nuttin' doin'!

PETE—Ready! (*The din is terrific.*)

DAVID (*indicating the instruments with some anxiety, and pulling* BILL'S *sleeve*)—Santa Claus, they haven't been boiled!

SLIM—W'at?

DAVID—They haven't been boiled, Mr. Slim!

SLIM (*and you know he means the children—not the toys*)—Dey oughta be!

PETE—All ready? Go! (*The uproar is repeated.*)

SLIM (*to* BILL)—An' I told yuh not to make a sound!

BILL—Say, kid, dere ain't nobody else on dis floor, is dere?

DAVID—No—nobody but us.

BILL (*drawing a sigh of relief*)—Dat's good. Now, fellers, we're gonna go ——

SLIM (*interrupting*)—An' we're gonna take him (*he indicates* DAVID) along with us.

BESSIE—W'at's de hurry, Bill?

PETE—We don't wanna go!

T'EODORE—Not now!

BESSIE—Bill, dere's no place fer us to go to.

BILL—W'at do yuh mean?

PETE—De landlord, he come along w'ile we was leavin', an' he says we needn't come back—none of us—never.

BESSIE (*rather pleased with her news*)—He says he'll put de furniture on de sidewalk, an' yuh can git it w'enever yuh like.

PETE—De sooner de better, he says.

BESSIE—Yea—an' dat wasn't all he says!

BILL (*aghast*)—He turn yuh out de moment my back was toined?

BESSIE—Yuh bet he did!

BILL—An what did paw say?

BESSIE—Paw says ef yuh can't support him in better style den dat, he's gonna quit yuh cold.

BILL—W'at do yuh t'ink of dat, Slim? Ain't it de limit?

DAVID (*seizing* BILL's *hand*)—What's the matter, Santa Claus?

BILL (*angrily*)—Aw, nuttin'!

DAVID—Why don't you tell me, Santa Claus?

BILL (*bitterly*)—Dere's nuttin' de matter—on'y de kids ain't gonna have a roof over deir heads tonight!

DAVID—Because you didn't get money?

BILL—Dat's w'y.

DAVID—And because you didn't pay the rent?

BILL—Yuh said it, kid.

DAVID—But why do you want a roof over their heads? Can't we take them along with us?

BILL—W'at's dat?

DAVID—They can come to the North Pole, too, can't they? Of course it will be a little crowded in the sleigh, but there'll be room for all of us.

SLIM (*meaningly*)—Do yuh hear dat, Bill?

DAVID (*eagerly*)—The reindeer are waiting outside!

SLIM—Aroun' de corner.

DAVID—Dancer and Prancer, and Blixen and Vixen ——

BILL (*interrupting*)—De reindeer's name is Lizzie—an' her radiator's froze.

SLIM (*crossing to him earnestly*)—But it's gonna get us away from here, Bill! We get outa de city—we go somew'eres in de Bronx—an' den we give Millman a ring on de telephone ——

DAVID—Don't telephone daddy; he's always busy.

SLIM—He won't be busy dis time. (*He argues with* BILL.)

DAVID—You don't know my daddy! My daddy is the busiest man in the world! When he comes to see me, he says, "Exactly ten"— and that means exactly ten. When I want to see him I have to ask his secretary—and sometimes he can't see me at all.

BESSIE—Do yuh like dat?

DAVID—I don't like it—but I guess daddy *has* to work.

BESSIE—Your daddy woik? W'at fer?

DAVID—I guess he wants *his* money—so that he can pay *his* rent. (BESSIE *snickers.* DAVID *bridles indignantly.*) Don't make fun of him! I won't let anybody do that! I don't think anybody works as hard as he works! Why, he starts in the morning before I get up, and sometimes when I wake in the middle of the night I tiptoe to the door of my room, and I can see the light burning in his study downstairs! Daddy works *hard*—and he looks so tired! He's so tired sometimes that he won't let me sit in his lap.

BESSIE—My daddy lets me sit in his lap all I like!

DAVID (*eagerly*)—Does everybody call him a fine man?

BESSIE (*a bit dubiously*)—Dey calls him all sorts of t'ings—but he don't mind dat.

DAVID—Do they send men to his house to take his picture?

BESSIE (*with pardonable pride*)—Dey don't have ter; dey got his pitcher at headquarters.

DAVID—Do the policemen stop and speak to him?

BESSIE—Not ef he sees dem foist.

BILL (*who has been arguing with* SLIM *in undertones during the preceding dialogue now turns abruptly*)—Come on, fellows! We're gonna go! (SLIM *takes* DAVID'S *hand.*)

A CHORUS—Naw, Bill! We wanna play wit' de presents! We don't wanna leave de presents! We want de presents!

BILL (*angrily*)—Come on, I say!

MAGGIE (*appealingly*)—Baby don't wanna leave de presents!

DAVID—Santa Claus, let them take the presents with them! (*As* SLIM *releases him in astonishment, he runs to the children.*) Here: you take this; and here's something for you; and you take one of the railroad-trains—don't forget the tracks—and you take the other one.

BILL (*dumfounded*)—Yuh're givin' away yer toys?

DAVID (*busy distributing gifts*)—They want them more than I do! (*He turns again to the children.*) Here: you can carry more than that! (ANNIE'S *arms are full already, but he piles toys on the heap.*) Put these on top. Take them along. (*To* PETE)—Do they let you ride a bicycle?

PETE—Sure t'ing!

DAVID—Then take this one. (*To* BESSIE)—Do they let you go coasting on a sled?

BESSIE—All I want—ef I gotta sled.

DAVID—Here's one for you. (*To* T'EODORE, *holding up a pair of boxing-gloves*)—Can you use them?

T'EODORE—Can a duck swim?

DAVID—Take them.

PETE (*to* BILL)—Hey, Bill, can I have de tennis racket?

BILL (*to* DAVID)—How about it?

DAVID (*and you see it hurts—and besides* PETE'S *arms are full*)—He wants it more than I do.

MAGGIE (*with a cry of delight*)—Gee! look w'at I found! Ice skates! See de ice skates, baby?

DAVID—Ice skates! (*He pauses; takes them in his hand; caresses them. This time it hurts very much indeed.*)

BILL (*almost savagely*)—W'at are yuh gonna do, kid?

DAVID (*smiling at* BILL)—I'm going to give them to her. (*He places them in* MAGGIE'S *hands.*) Take good care of them—and look out for the baby—they're sharp. (*He turns to* BILL.) And now, Santa Claus, what's a kidnapping party?

BILL—Yuh wanna know dat?

DAVID—Yes, Santa Claus.

BILL—Yuh really wanna know? (DAVID *takes his hand and nods eagerly.* BILL *hesitates. Then he glares defiantly at* SLIM, *and turns to* DAVID.) Kid, yuh ain't never gonna loin dat from me!

SLIM (*with hostility*)—W'at did yuh say?

DAVID (*apologetically*)—I didn't mean to forget your present, Mr. Slim. (*He runs to the tree and fetches the candy.*) Here you are! And Merry Christmas! (*He gives* SLIM *the box.*)

SLIM—De candy! Dat's my idee of one fine present!

DAVID—And now, Santa Claus?

BILL (*shaking his head*)—Kid, it's gonna cost me a lotta coin—an', gee! w'at wouldn't I do wit' just a coupla dollars? but youse a little gentleman—see?—an' ef anybody lays a finger on yuh, I'll moider him! (*He casts a defiant glance at* SLIM *and claps his arm upon* DAVID's *shoulders in a rough accolade.*) Kid, youse a good sport—(*He bows grotesquely.*)—an' I take me hat off to yuh! Yours truly, John W. Santa!

SLIM (*gasping*)—Youse gonna leave him here?

BILL—Yuh hoid me.

SLIM—But we come here to ——

BILL (*interrupting*)—I changed my mind—see? A guy dat's a he-man can do dat t'ing—an' John W. Santa's a he-man! (*He indicates* DAVID.) I'm gonna leave him here—an' me an' de kids is gonna beat it—an' youse is comin' along, too; don't yuh forget dat!

SLIM—Bill! Yuh said yuh was hard-boiled!

BILL (*crossing to him menacingly*)—Ef yuh don't believe it, now's de time to try me! (*He pauses.*) Well?

(*There is sudden loud knocking at the locked door at the right.*)

HALLIGAN (*outside*)—Let me in! Let me in or I'll break down the door!

SLIM—Beat it! (*There is a rush for the windows, but it stops short as the door at the left, which has been ajar for some moments, suddenly opens, and* MILLMAN *stands on the threshold.*)

BILL (*rising nobly to the occasion*)—A-choo!

DAVID—God bless you!

SLIM—We're pinched!

MILLMAN (*quietly*)—Just that.

SLIM (*jerking his thumb toward the window*)—Cops outside?

MILLMAN (*nodding*)—They saw you come in. They've been waiting for you to come out.

ANNIE (*beginning to cry*)—I want my presents!

HALLIGAN (*hammering at the door again*)—Let me in!

MILLMAN—Let him in. (BILL *crosses to the door and unlocks it.* HALLIGAN *and* VICKY, *both wabbly, but on their feet again, come into the room.*)

VICKY—Master David! Master David! They haven't hurt you, have they? (*She rushes to him.*)

DAVID—Santa Claus wouldn't hurt anybody. He was going to give me a kidnapping party, that was all. (*He pats* BILL'*s hand.*)

VICKY (*horrified*)—Master David!

HALLIGAN (*producing a whistle*)—Shall I whistle for the police, sir?

MILLMAN—Wait, Halligan. (*He turns to the intruders.*) The house is surrounded. There is no way you can get out.

BILL (*most unhappily*)—Yes, sir. (*He takes off his mask. For the first time we see his face; the face of a half-starved lad with big eyes.*)

MILLMAN—Bear that in mind. (*Most unaccountably, most leisurely, he turns his back on* BILL, *and draws up a chair.*) Davy, how would you like to sit in my lap?

DAVID—I'd love it, Daddy!

MILLMAN—So would I. (DAVID *rushes to him.* MILLMAN *settles him comfortably, quite oblivious of the others.*) There. There. David, where were you going with this man?

DAVID—Not "this man," Daddy: it's Santa Claus.

MILLMAN—I meant Santa Claus.

DAVID—I was just going to the North Pole.

MILLMAN—Were you going to leave me alone?

DAVID—I would have come back tomorrow or the next day, Daddy.

MILLMAN—Are you sure, Davy?

DAVID—Well, pretty sure. (*He hesitates.*) I wouldn't want to bother you if you were busy.

MILLMAN (*wincingly*)—I'm not so busy as you think, Davy.

DAVID—No?

MILLMAN—No. (*He pauses.*) Sometimes, when a man's lonely— when he misses somebody who's gone terribly, terribly much—he tries to make himself busy. Do you understand that, Davy?

DAVID—I think I do. You mean—mummy.

MILLMAN—I mean—mummy. (*His voice lightens.*)—But now

that my little boy is growing older, I don't expect to be nearly so busy any more.

DAVID (*ecstatically*)—Really, Daddy?

MILLMAN—Honest and truly!

DAVID (*turning to* BILL)—Did you hear that, Santa Claus? (BILL *shuffles his feet and does not answer.*)

MILLMAN (*sharply*)—Did you hear that, Santa Claus?

BILL—Yes, sir. I hoid him.

MILLMAN (*trying to speak lightly*)—And now, if you still want to go to the North Pole with Santa Claus—you may go. (*He pauses.*) Do you want to go?

DAVID (*hesitates; he rises; looks at his father; looks at* BILL— *and then, to his father's unutterable horror, runs to* BILL)—You won't mind, will you, Santa Claus? (BILL *is silent.*)

MILLMAN (*in a tone like that of a whip-lash*)—Answer him!

BILL (*addressing* DAVID, *and exceedingly gruff*)—W'at do yuh mean, kid?

DAVID—You won't mind if I stay here, will you? I don't care so much about that old North Pole.

VICKY (*tremulous with joy*)—Davy! Davy, boy!

BILL (*a mighty effort*)—A-choo-oo ——

HALLIGAN (*after a pause*)—Shall I take them away now, Mr. Millman?

MILLMAN—Yes, Halligan.

HALLIGAN (*gruffly*)—Come on, you! (*He herds them toward the door.*)

DAVID—Don't forget the presents!

MILLMAN—No; don't forget the presents! (*The children need no second invitation. They take up the gifts, as many as they can carry in great haste. But there are more than they can carry un- aided.*) Help them, Halligan.

HALLIGAN (*surprized, but doing as he is told*)—Yes, sir. (*And* VICKY *helps without being told. The children begin to file out at the door.*)

DAVID (*halting* BESSIE, *who is next to last*)—Take the sled!

BESSIE (*taking it*)—Much obliged.

DAVID (*stopping* MAGGIE *and the baby*)—You're forgetting the skates! (DAVID *gives them to her.*)

MAGGIE—T'anks. Come, baby. (*She goes, followed by* VICKY.)

HALLIGAN (*burdened with gifts, stands in the doorway, and crooks his finger at* BILL *and* SLIM)—Come on!

DAVID—You're forgetting your candy, Mr. Slim!

SLIM (*refusing to take it*)—I never seen dat box before in all my life! (*He goes quickly.*)

BILL (*after a brief hesitation*)—Give it here, kid. (DAVID *gives him the box.* BILL *turns apologetically to* MILLMAN.) 'Tain't safe to leave dat stuff around.

MILLMAN (*gravely*)—Why not?

BILL (*hesitates again; then he squares his shoulders*)—De candy's loaded wit' knock-out drops. (*There is a sharp intake of breath from* HALLIGAN, *but his employer is not surprised.*)

MILLMAN (*quietly*)—I guessed as much. (*He halts* BILL *as the latter turns to go.*) You came here intending to kidnap my boy?

BILL (*reluctantly*)—Yes, sir.

MILLMAN—You could have done it?

BILL—Yes, sir.

MILLMAN—Why didn't you do it? (BILL *hesitates.*) Out with it!

BILL (*raising his head, and looking* MILLMAN *in the eye*)—He was nice to de kids—see? He give 'em all his presents. He didn't hold out none fer himself. He's de foist guy dat ever treated 'em like dey was human. I'd lay down me life fer him after he done dat! (*He pauses, and continues hesitantly.*) Yuh see, paw don't woik reg'lar; an' maw's sick, an' ever sence I been old enough to go out on de street an' sell papers, I've been keepin' de kids alive— an' dere's eight of 'em now. (*Once more he raises his head.*) He treated 'em square, see?—an' I, I done de same by him.

MILLMAN (*after a pause*)—You know where my office is?

BILL (*puzzled*)—Yes, sir.

MILLMAN—Come and see me tomorrow. (*He turns to* HALLIGAN.) This gentleman will leave my house as a gentleman ought to leave it. You will show him to the door. You will see to it that the police do not molest him. You will send for my car. And you will tell my chauffeur to drive him home. (HALLIGAN *bows silently.*)

BILL (*overwhelmed*)—Mr. Millman!

DAVID—Daddy, Santa Claus has no home to go to.

MILLMAN (*smiling*)—I forgot. (*He produces an envelope from his pocket.*) I listened at the door for ten minutes before I came in. I heard every word that was spoken. (*He claps* BILL *heartily on the shoulder, and extends his hand—and in it is the same envelope that hung on the tree.*) Merry Christmas, my friend!

BILL (*wiping his hand on his trousers leg before taking* MILLMAN'S, *and painfully embarrassed*)—De same to youse, Mr. Millman, an' de same, an' lots of 'em, to de little gen'leman.

DAVID—Thanks, Santa Claus.

(BILL *goes, followed by* HALLIGAN. *The door clicks shut after them. For a second father and son gaze at each other in silence. Then:*

MILLMAN—I gave him your aunt Mary's envelop.

DAVID—I know you did, Daddy.

(*The two gaze at each other, wishing to say much, but unable to break through their masculine reserve.* MILLMAN *inspects the stripped tree with elaborate care.* DAVID *does likewise.*)

MILLMAN (*at length*)—Christmas is over, Davy.

(*From downstairs comes a joyful din; the blare of toy trumpets, the jingling of* BESSIE'S *sleigh-bells, the shouting and the laughter of children.* MILLMAN *turns his head to listen; opens the door to hear better.* DAVID *goes to his side, takes his hand, and listens with him.*)

DAVID—Christmas has just begun.

(*The joyful din grows louder—louder.*)

THE CURTAIN FALLS

The Seventh Christmas[1]

By Coningsby Dawson

CHARACTERS (of the main play)
MARY—mother of Jesus
JOSEPH—an old carpenter
JESUS
BALTHAZAR—the third king
A VILLAGE CHILD

Scene (of the main play) : *The cottage in Nazareth. This is a shallow set, arranged so that a curtain at the rear can be drawn, revealing the inner stage. Joseph is working at a table in the back left, and at the side front is a crude bench. At the right about halfway back is a chest. There is a dim light as of late afternoon or early evening. Mary is seated at the bench, looking through the doorway at the right.*

CHARACTERS (of the inner play)
MARY
AN ANGEL
JOSEPH—younger than in the main play
FOUR SHEPHERDS
MELCHIOR (old, with a white beard)
CASPAR (middle aged, black beard)
BALTHAZAR (young)

[1] Coningsby Dawson's *Seventh Christmas* has long been one of Uncle Toby's favorite short stories. It is here made available to the general public in dramatic form for the first time. This play, in its printed form, is designed for the reading public only. All dramatic, motion-picture, and other rights in it are fully protected by copyright. No performance, professional or amateur, nor any radio broadcast, nor any public reading or recitation may be given without permission, in advance, of the author's agents, Paul R. Reynolds & Son, 599 Fifth Avenue, New York, N. Y. This adaptation is made by Alice Moss.

Scene (of the inner stage) : *The inner stage is made simply of dark-blue curtains on three sides. The only property is a bench, and although it is not imperative, a box with hay to represent the manger in one scene.*

MARY—It is his seventh birthday and I have no presents to give him. There is hardly enough food for us all. And yet the angels sang "Glory in the highest." Was it not so, Joseph?

JOSEPH—Art thou sure the angels sang? It seems so like a distant dream. There have been no signs since then.

MARY—No, there have been no signs since then, and yet the wise men and shepherds did come. The three caskets are a proof of that. We still have them.

JOSEPH (*wearily*)—Aye. Wilt thou not consent to sell those caskets? A traveling merchant would give much for them and we might then have food. Mary, they are worth a king's ransom. If we were to sell ——

MARY (*sorrowfully*)—And wouldst thou sell his ransom without our King's knowledge? After all, when they are gone what token have we that my son is King? On the day when royal messengers shall come for him from Jerusalem, how else shall they know that my story is true? Nay, Joseph, it is better to be poor and hungry than to sell the gifts of the Eastern Kings.

JOSEPH—Perhaps thou art right. I must try to finish this ox yoke to give thee food. I am old and forgetful. Do not let me sleep.

(*Enter* JESUS *who sings "The Lord is my Shepherd, I shall not want . . ." etc.*)

JOSEPH—I am weary and it is so hard.

JESUS (*wistfully, standing beside* JOSEPH)—I wish I might help, Father.

MARY—Nay, little one, thou art too young. But thou canst aid by keeping him awake as he has asked.

(*Child runs in at the door. Shouts merrily.*)

CHILD—Come out, Jesus, come and play king. We shall make thee a crown and thou shalt sing to us. Come out; the boys are waiting.

JESUS (*smiles and shakes his head*)—No, not today.

JOSEPH (*half to himself*)—I have toiled on this for many days and yet it is not done. I fear my eye is not as clear as it was, and my hand has lost its cunning. I grow so weary, so weary.

CHILD—My father says that thou wert once a fine carpenter, but the hot suns have made thee old, and thou shouldst not have gone to Egypt.

JESUS—Why didst thou go to Egypt, Father?

JOSEPH (*as though defending himself*)—It was all for thee.

JESUS—Tell me about it, Father.

JOSEPH—Nay, son, when thou art older. Thou wouldst laugh and not believe were I to tell thee now.

CHILD—Do come and play with us, Jesus.

JESUS—No, not today.

(*Exit Child*)

JOSEPH—I am so weary, I cannot do it. I cannot —— (*His head falls on the table and he goes to sleep.*)

MARY (*whispers*)—Wake him, dear, as he has asked thee. He wished very much to finish this work today.

JESUS (*also whispers*)—He is so tired. (*Comes close and throws his arms around* MARY.) I will stay and protect thee, Mother, but Father shall sleep. I wish that I could help him.

MARY—Nay, little one, thou art too young.

JESUS—But I am seven years old today and almost a man. Hast thou forgotten? (*He sits beside her.*)

MARY—No, dear, but since I had no gift for thee, I hoped thou wouldst not remember.

JESUS—But I do remember, Mother, I am seven years old (*leans his head against her breast*).

MARY (*dreamily*)—It was not always thus. Seven years ago—I know a story of a king who is seven years old today.

JESUS—Tell me, Mother.

MARY—Nay, when thou art older. Thou wouldst laugh and not believe were I to tell thee now.

JESUS (*eagerly*)—Oh, tell me.

MARY—Well, since I have no gift for thee I will tell thee the story of this king. I knew his mother. Does it seem strange to thee, little Jesus, that I should know the mother of a boy who is to be king? (*She kisses his forehead and slips her arm around him.*) But this is a strange tale.

JESUS—But how does she know her son is going to be a king?

MARY—An angel came down from heaven one day while she was in the garden and told her she had been chosen to be the mother of the Lord. If thou wilt listen carefully I shall tell thee all that he told to her, and while I talk try to form in thy mind a picture of what I say.

> (*Curtain of the Inner Stage is drawn open. In the center the* MARY *of the Inner Stage, hereafter referred to as* MARY *I. S., is seated. As the curtain opens, the* ANGEL *enters right.* MARY *I. S., kneels.*)

ANGEL—Hail thou that art highly favoured. The Lord is with thee. Blessed art thou among women. Fear not, for thou hast found favour with God and behold thou shalt bring forth a son. He shall be great and shall be called the Son of the Highest, and the Lord shall give unto him the throne of his father, David, and of his kingdom there shall be no end.

MARY (*Inner Stage*)—Behold the handmaid of the Lord. Be it unto me according to thy word.

> (*Curtain of the Inner Stage*)

MARY—There was a carpenter of the village where she lived who loved her and every day he carried her pitcher for her from the well. The morning after the angel had come to her, the carpenter watched for her to pass, and when she did not go to draw water at the well, he came in search of her. She was still sitting in the garden where the angel had left her, gazing straight before her; for to be the mother of a king is very blessed, but it is very terrible to be the mother of the Son of God. Then the carpenter asked her why she had not been to draw water. Now though he was a good man, he had never seen an angel ——

JOSEPH (*stirring in his sleep*)—I cannot—I cannot.

JESUS—And because he had never seen an angel ——?

MARY—Because he was a good man, he came to understand. Through the summer they lived very happily. In the evenings in the garden the carpenter carved a royal cradle, with cherubim upon it, and she wove robes in preparation for the King's coming. Then in the winter, just before he should be born, a decree went out from Cæsar that all the people should go home to their own cities to be taxed. So the carpenter, who came from a distant town, brought a donkey and set her upon it and they started for Jerusalem.

JESUS—But, Mother, didn't she ride on a camel covered with silks and jewels like a great princess?

MARY (*bowing her head*)—Nay, little one, I said that this was a strange story. Because her son was not yet king she rode on a donkey and the carpenter walked beside her. It was a difficult journey and she grew very weary.

JESUS (*lifting his arms and drawing* MARY'S *face down to him*) —If I had been there, Mother, I would have helped thee.

MARY (*startled*)—Thou hast guessed, little Jesus?

JESUS—Yes, Mother, I have guessed. But tell me more. I have wished so much to know about the beautiful caskets and why thou didst go into Egypt.

MARY—I will tell thee, then, as I have often longed to do. At last we reached Jerusalem, the great city of the temple, thronged with people and caravans. But we did not stop, for Joseph had kinsmen in Bethlehem not far away. We plodded on, though the donkey stumbled at every step and Joseph was weary and footsore. Finally we reached the little city of David, but from every door came the words "Had we only known sooner we should have found a place for thee, but there is not room." Even at the inn there was no place left for us. When I could bear it no longer we found behind the inn a little cave where the cattle were stalled. The beasts made way for us, and I found a soft bed in the hay. It was there thou wast born. I wrapped thee in swaddling clothes and laid thee in a manger because there was no room for thee in the abodes of men. No room for the Son of God.

(*Voices outside sing "It Came upon a Midnight Clear"* [*see page 164*], *and the curtain of the inner stage is drawn.*)

(MARY, *I. S., is seated with the child in her arms and* JOSEPH *stands behind her. Enter the four* SHEPHERDS *slowly.*)

JESUS—Who were those men who came, Mother?

MARY—Dost thou remember how two years ago on thy birthday a shepherd from afar off brought thee a little lamb? He is one of those who came when thou wast born. Dost thou recall him now?

JESUS—Yes, now I remember him. But why did he come there to the cave so long ago?

MARY—Hush, dear, and I will tell thee.

(SHEPHERDS *kneel before* MARY, *I. S.*)

MARY (*I. S.*)—Why do you kneel to me, good shepherds?

FIRST SHEPHERD—Oh, blessed woman, as we lay in the fields, keeping watch over our flocks by night, the angel of the Lord came upon us and glory shone round about us and we were sore afraid. But the angel said unto us, "Fear not, for behold, I bring you good tidings of great joy which shall be to all people. For unto you is born this day in the City of David a Savior which is Christ, the Lord. And this shall be a sign unto you: You shall find the babe wrapped in swaddling clothes and lying in a manger."

SECOND SHEPHERD—And suddenly there was with the angel a multitude of heavenly host praising God and saying, "Glory to God in the highest and on earth peace, good will toward men." When the angels had returned to heaven we left our flocks and came with haste and found thee.

MARY (*I. S.*)—Good shepherds, I thank you.

(SHEPHERDS *kneel again and kiss the child reverently, then rise and back out slowly. As they go voices outside sing "We Three Kings of Orient Are"* [*see page 165*]).

JESUS—What is that, Mother?

MARY—Listen, it is the three Eastern kings.

KINGS (*outside*)—Where is he that is born King of the Jews, for we have seen his star in the East and are come to worship him.

PEOPLE (*outside*)—There is no king in Judea. We know no king save Herod.

(JOSEPH, *I.S., moves toward the right and peers out.*)

KINGS—We have followed his star hither. It hath led us from the East. For many nights it hath moved before us. Tell us where he lies.

PEOPLE—There is no king here. Perhaps in Jerusalem ——

KINGS—The star, the star! It hath come down from heaven and rests above the stable in the courtyard! Make way! We have found him. (*Stamping is heard and the* KINGS *enter upon the Inner Stage and bow low to the ground.*)

MARY (*I. S.*)—My lords, whence are ye come to me?

BALTHAZAR—Mother of Mothers, in our homes in the East we have long waited for thy son to be born, for our prophet foretold his coming. When his star appeared we rode forth and have come hither, bearing presents.

MELCHIOR—I, Melchior, give a crown of gold unto thy son as a sign of Power.

CASPAR—I, Caspar, lay at thy feet my offering of frankincense. The East yields it unto him for Worship.

BALTHAZAR (*sadly*)—I, Balthazar, bring myrrh, which signifieth Death—a gift to every man of woman born.

(*Voices outside sing "Glory to God in the highest and on earth peace, good will toward men." Curtain of Inner Stage.*)

MARY—Then, little one, these kings, since the inn refused thee shelter, raised their tents in the courtyard. And while they slept they were warned by a vision to depart and go home another way. So in the morning they arose and left by ships from Tarshish. And to Joseph also came an angel saying, "Arise, take the young child and escape into Egypt, for Herod is seeking his life." So we, too, arose and left. Herod, unable to find thee, put all the young children in Bethlehem to death, and from the town and the hills came the cry of mothers weeping for their children.

JESUS—But why did he wish to kill me, Mother?

MARY—Because of the question that the kings had asked, calling thee the King of the Jews.

JESUS—It is the game at which I play with the village boys. Mother, but am I ——?

MARY (*putting her finger over his lips*)—Thou art a child, the son of Mary. Herod was not good; he feared lest God should wrest his throne from him.

JESUS (*laughing*)—And dost thou think that when I am a man I shall take his throne from him?

MARY (*draws him closer to her*)—Hush, dear. I do not know. But let me finish my story. We went to Egypt, taking with us the golden caskets the kings had brought. In Egypt work was hard to find; the roads were hot and Joseph grew old through poverty. Then word came to us that Herod was dead, so we returned to the carpenter's shop with naught left to us of all these glories save only the golden caskets. The rest thou knowest.

JESUS—Mother, it is my birthday. Let me look into the caskets.

MARY—It can do no harm. Come hither.

(*They cross to the chest. MARY opens it and takes out the three caskets and a little white silk robe.*)

MARY—This I made for thee, little one, in readiness for the day when they shall come to crown thee.

(*She puts the robe on him and places the crown on his head.*)

MARY—This is for power. (*Scatters incense.*) This is for worship. (*She looks at the third casket, thrusts it quickly behind her without opening it, and puts her arms about him, kneeling.*)

My soul doth magnify the Lord and my spirit hath rejoiced in God. (*Sound of hoofs outside. She rises and goes to the door.*)

BALTHAZAR (*breathlessly, outside*)—Where is he? Where is he who was born king? Once when I was young, on such a night as this I found him. Tonight there are many stars, but no star to guide me.

MARY—Whom seekest thou?

BALTHAZAR—I seek a child of holy birth whom I found seven years ago when I was young, Melchior was old, and Caspar was midway between us. Now Melchior is dying. We have heard no more of the child, so without a star to guide me, because my faith is greatest, I have journeyed forth. Where is he who is born King of the Jews? If thou canst tell me I will give thee—(*pauses*). But I can give thee nothing, for I have spent my all in the searching.

(MARY *motions toward* JESUS *standing beside the chest.*)

BALTHAZAR—It is true. It is true. (*Kneeling and taking the child in his arms.*) I came to thee before with a lordly train but now I come empty-handed. What is there I can give thee?

JESUS (*stroking his face*)—It is my seventh birthday, and my mother is hungry.

BALTHAZAR—At least I have food. (*Unrolls a bundle and takes out bread and dates. They eat.*) Were I in my own country I would give thee a palace of white marble, with fountains playing and hanging gardens and slaves to serve thee. Here I am poor; but such as I have I give thee.

JESUS (*sings softly*)—The Lord is my shepherd; I shall not want.

BALTHAZAR—I would learn thy song that I might return to my own people and say "It is thus that the little Jesus singeth."

MARY—But thou must hasten back. Melchior is old and dying. It is a long journey. What can we send to him to make him certain?

BALTHAZAR—Not the crown, for it was his gift.

MARY—The frankincense is all gone.

JESUS—Then let us send him the third casket, for it hath not been opened. But first I will open it, for it was thy gift. (*Reaches for the casket.*)

MARY (*alarmed and trying to hold him back*)—Nay, little one!
(*Before she can stop him* JESUS *has thrown back the lid. The room is flooded with light. They all look upward to where a star now shines, as if it had risen from the casket.* JESUS *laughs and claps his hands.*)

BALTHAZAR—The star! The star we had lost! It shall guide me back to my dying friend and show him that my story is true.

(*Embraces* JESUS. *As he goes out she puts her arms around* JESUS *and looks at him for a moment in silence.*)

MARY—Thou didst bring back the lost star. Thou hast proved that which I so often doubt. Thou art indeed the Son of God. (*Rises and goes to look down at the sleeping* JOSEPH.)

JESUS (*takes off the crown and puts it in the chest*)—I am thy son also, Mother. (*Moves softly to the work-table and begins to work with* JOSEPH's *tools.*) I am seven and almost a man.

11

Two Distinguished Christmas Sermons, Each in Its Own Way Presenting Anew the Message That Has Endured Two Thousand Years.

Keeping Christmas

By HENRY VAN DYKE

He that regardeth the day, regardeth it unto the Lord.
—ROMANS, XIV: 6.

IT IS a good thing to observe Christmas Day. The mere marking of times and seasons, when men agree to stop work and make merry together, is a wise and wholesome custom. It helps one to feel the supremacy of the common life over the individual life. It reminds a man to set his own little watch, now and then, by the great clock of humanity which runs on sun time.

But there is a better thing than the observance of Christmas Day, and that is, keeping Christmas.

Are you willing to forget what you have done for other people, and to remember what other people have done for you; to ignore what the world owes you, and to think what you owe the world; to put your rights in the background and your duties in the middle distance, and your chances to do a little more than your duty in the foreground; to see that your fellow-men are just as real as you are, and try to look behind their faces to their hearts, hungry for joy; to own that probably the only good reason for your existence is not what you are going to get out of life, but what you are going to give to life; to close your book of complaints against the management of the universe, and look around you for a place where you can sow a few seeds of happiness—are you willing to do these things even for a day? Then you can keep Christmas.

Are you willing to stoop down and consider the needs and the desires of little children; to remember the weakness and loneliness of people who are growing old; to stop asking how much your friends love you, and ask yourself whether you love them enough; to bear in mind the things that other people have to bear on their hearts; to try to understand what those who live in the same house with you really want, without waiting for them to tell you; to trim your lamp so that it will give more light and less smoke; and to carry it in front so that your shadow will fall behind you; to make a grave for your ugly thoughts, and a garden for your kindly feelings, with the gate open—are you willing to do these things even for a day? Then you can keep Christmas.

Are you willing to believe that love is the strongest thing in the world—stronger than hate, stronger than evil, stronger than death—and that the blessed life which began in Bethlehem nineteen hundred years ago is the image and brightness of the Eternal Love? Then you can keep Christmas.

And if you keep it for a day, why not always?

But you can never keep it alone.

Good Tidings of Great Joy

By Cardinal Newman

*"And the angel said unto them, Fear not: for, behold,
I bring you good tidings of great joy, which shall be to
all people. For unto you is born this day in the city of
David a Saviour, which is Christ the Lord."*
—LUKE II: 10, 11.

THERE are two principal lessons which we are taught on the
great Festival which we this day celebrate—lowliness and joy.
This surely is a day, of all others, in which is set before us the
heavenly excellence and the acceptableness in God's sight of that
state which most men have, or may have, allotted to them: humble
or private life, and cheerfulness in it. If we consult the writings
of historians, philosophers, and poets of this world, we shall be
led to think great men happy. But when we think of this day's
Festival, and what we commemorate upon it, a new and very
different scene opens upon us. First, we are reminded that though
this life must ever be a life of toil and effort, yet that, properly
speaking, we have not to seek our highest good. It is found, it is
brought near us, in the descent of the Son of God from His
Father's bosom to this world. It is stored up among us on earth.
No longer need men of ardent minds wander about and encounter
peril in quest of that unknown blessedness to which their hearts
naturally aspire, as they did in heathen times. The text speaks to
them and to all. "Unto you," it says, "is born this day in the city
of David a Saviour, which is Christ the Lord."

Nor, again, need we go in quest of any of those things which
this vain world calls great and noble. Christ altogether dishonored
what the world esteems, when He took on Himself a rank and
station which the world despises. No lot could be more humble
and more ordinary than that which the Son of God chose for
Himself.

So that we have on the Feast of the Nativity these two lessons —instead of anxiety within and despondence without, instead of a weary search after great things—to be cheerful and joyful; and, again, to be so in the midst of those obscure and ordinary circumstances of life which the world passes over and thinks scorn of.

The shepherds were chosen on account of their lowliness to be the first to hear of the Lord's nativity, a secret which none of the princes of this world knew. The angels who excel in strength, these did His bidding towards the shepherds. Here the highest and the lowest of God's rational creatures are brought together. A set of poor men, engaged in a life of hardship, exposed at that very time to the cold and darkness of the night, watching their flocks, with the view of scaring away beasts of prey or robbers. To men so circumstanced the angel appeared, to open their minds, and to teach them not to be downcast and in bondage because they were low in the world.

The angel honoured a humble lot by his very appearing to the shepherds; next he taught it to be joyful by his message. The angel said, "Fear not," when he saw the alarm which his presence caused among the shepherds. Even a lesser wonder would have reasonably startled them. Therefore the angel said, "Fear not." We are naturally afraid of any messenger from the other world, for we have an uneasy conscience when left to ourselves, and think that his coming forebodes evil. Besides, we so little realize the unseen world, that were angel or spirit to present himself before us we should be startled by reason of our unbelief, a truth being brought home to our minds which we never apprehended before. So for one or other reason the shepherds were sore afraid when the glory of the Lord shone round about them. And the angel said, "Fear not." A little religion makes us afraid; when a little light is poured in upon the conscience, there is a darkness visible; nothing but sights of woe and terror; the glory of God alarms while it shines around. His holiness, the range and difficulties of His commandments, the greatness of His power, the faithfulness of His word, frighten the sinner, and men seeing him afraid, think religion has made him so, whereas he is not yet religious at all. "Fear not," said the angel; "for, behold, I bring you good tidings of great joy, which shall be to all people. For unto you is born this day in the city of David a Saviour, which is Christ the Lord." And then, when he had finished his announcement, "suddenly there was with the angel a multitude of the heavenly host praising God, and saying, Glory to God in the highest, and on earth peace, good will toward men."

Surely the lesson of Joy which the Incarnation gives us is as impressive as the lesson of humility. St. Paul gives us the one lesson in his Epistle to the Philippians: "Let this mind be in you, which was also in Christ Jesus: Who, being in the form of God, thought it not robbery to be equal with God: But made himself of no reputation, and took upon him the form of a servant, and was made in the likeness of men:" and St. Peter gives us the lesson of joyfulness: "Whom having not seen, ye love; in whom, though now ye see him not, yet believing, ye rejoice with joy unspeakable, and full of glory: Receiving the end of your faith, even the salvation of your souls."

Take these thoughts with you, my brethren, to your homes on this festive day; let them be with you in your family and social meetings. It is a day of joy: it is good to be joyful—it is wrong to be otherwise. For one day we may put off the burden of our polluted consciences, and rejoice in the perfections of our Saviour Christ, without thinking of ourselves, without thinking of our own miserable uncleanness; but contemplating His glory, His righteousness, His purity, His majesty, His overflowing love. We may rejoice in the Lord, and in all His creatures see Him. We may enjoy His temporal bounty, and partake of the pleasant things of earth with Him in our thoughts; we may rejoice in our friends for His sake, loving them most especially because He has loved them.

"God has not appointed us unto wrath, but to obtain salvation through our Lord Jesus Christ, who died for us, that whether we wake or sleep, we should live together with Him." Let us seek the grace of a cheerful heart, an even temper, sweetness, gentleness, and brightness of mind, as walking in His light, and by His grace. Let us pray Him to give us the spirit of ever-abundant, ever-springing love, which overpowers and sweeps away the vexations of life by its own richness and strength, and which above all things unites us to Him who is the fountain and the centre of all mercy, loving-kindness, and joy.

12

The Story of the Nativity As It
Is Told in the New Testament,
With Appropriate Prayers for Sol-
emnizing Christmas in the Home.

The Bible Story of the Nativity

Selections from the Gospels Arranged to Form a Consecutive Narrative of the First Christmas

LUKE 1:

26   And in the sixth month the angel Gabriel was sent from God unto a city of Galilee, named Nazareth.

27   To a virgin espoused to a man whose name was Joseph, of the house of David; and the virgin's name *was* Mary.

28   And the angel came in unto her, and said, Hail, *thou that art* highly favoured, the Lord *is* with thee: blessed *art* thou among women.

29   And when she saw *him*, she was troubled at his saying, and cast in her mind what manner of salutation this should be.

30   And the angel said unto her, Fear not, Mary: for thou hast found favour with God.

31   And, behold, thou shalt conceive in thy womb, and bring forth a son, and shalt call his name JESUS.

32   He shall be great, and shall be called the Son of the Highest: and the Lord God shall give unto him the throne of his father David:

33   And he shall reign over the house of Jacob for ever; and of his kingdom there shall be no end.

34   Then said Mary unto the angel, How shall this be, seeing I know not a man?

35   And the angel answered and said unto her, The Holy Ghost shall come upon thee, and the power of the Highest shall overshadow thee: therefore also that holy thing which shall be born of thee shall be called the Son of God.

36   And, behold, thy cousin Elizabeth, she hath also conceived a son in her old age: and this is the sixth month with her, who was called barren.

37   For with God nothing shall be impossible.

38   And Mary said, Behold the handmaid of the Lord; be it unto me according to thy word. And the angel departed from her.

46   And Mary said, My soul doth magnify the Lord,

47   And my spirit hath rejoiced in God my Saviour.

48   For he hath regarded the low estate of his handmaiden: for, behold, from henceforth all generations shall call me blessed.

49   For he that is mighty hath done to me great things; and holy *is* his name.

50   And his mercy *is* on them that fear him from generation to generation.

51   He hath shewed strength with his arm; he hath scattered the proud in the imagination of their hearts.

52   He hath put down the mighty from *their* seats, and exalted them of low degree.

53   He hath filled the hungry with good things; and the rich he hath sent empty away.

54   He hath holpen his servant Israel, in remembrance of *his* mercy;

55   As he spake to our fathers, to Abraham, and to his seed for ever.

MATTHEW I:

18   Now the birth of Jesus Christ was on this wise: When as his mother Mary was espoused to Joseph, before they came together, she was found with child of the Holy Ghost.

19   Then Joseph her husband, being a just *man*, and not willing to make her a publick example, was minded to put her away privily.

20   But while he thought on these things, behold, the angel of the Lord appeared unto him in a dream, saying, Joseph, thou son of David, fear not to take unto thee Mary thy wife: for that which is conceived in her is of the Holy Ghost.

21   And she shall bring forth a son, and thou shalt call his name JESUS: for he shall save his people from their sins.

LUKE II:

1   And it came to pass in those days, that there went out a decree from Cæsar Augustus, that all the world should be taxed.

2   (*And* this taxing was first made when Cyrenius was governor of Syria.)

3   And all went to be taxed, every one into his own city.

4   And Joseph also went up from Galilee, out of the city of Nazareth, into Judæa, unto the city of David, which is called Bethlehem; (because he was of the house and lineage of David:)

5   To be taxed with Mary his espoused wife, being great with child.

6   And so it was, that, while they were there, the days were accomplished that she should be delivered.

7   And she brought forth her firstborn son, and wrapped him in swaddling clothes, and laid him in a manger; because there was no room for them in the inn.

8   And there were in the same country shepherds abiding in the field, keeping watch over their flock by night.

9   And, lo, the angel of the Lord came unto them, and the glory of the Lord shone round about them: and they were sore afraid.

10   And the angel said unto them, Fear not: for, behold, I bring you good tidings of great joy, which shall be to all people.

11   For unto you is born this day in the city of David a Saviour which is Christ the Lord.

12   And this *shall be* a sign unto you; Ye shall find the babe wrapped in swaddling clothes, lying in a manger.

13   And suddenly there was with the angel a multitude of the heavenly host praising God, and saying,

14   Glory to God in the highest, and on earth peace, good will toward men.

15   And it came to pass, as the angels were gone away from them into heaven, the shepherds said one to another, Let us now go even unto Bethlehem, and see this thing which is come to pass, which the Lord hath made known unto us.

16   And they came with haste, and found Mary, and Joseph, and the babe lying in a manger.

17   And when they had seen *it*, they made known abroad the saying which was told them concerning this child.

18   And all they that heard *it* wondered at those things which were told them by the shepherds.

19   But Mary kept all these things, and pondered *them* in her heart.

20   And the shepherds returned, glorifying and praising God for all the things that they had heard and seen, as it was told unto them.

MATTHEW II:

1   Now when Jesus was born in Bethlehem of Judæa in the days of Herod the king, behold, there came wise men from the east to Jerusalem,

2   Saying, Where is he that is born King of the Jews? For we have seen his star in the east, and are come to worship him.

3   When Herod the king had heard *these things*, he was troubled, and all Jerusalem with him.

4   And when he had gathered all the chief priests and scribes of the people together, he demanded of them where Christ should be born.

5   And they said unto him, In Bethlehem of Judæa: for thus it is written by the prophet,

6   And thou Bethlehem, *in* the land of Juda, art not the least among the princes of Juda: for out of thee shall come a Governor, that shall rule my people Israel.

7   Then Herod, when he had privily called the wise men, enquired of them diligently what time the star appeared.

8   And he sent them to Bethlehem, and said, Go and search diligently for the young child; and when ye have found *him*, bring me word again, that I may come and worship him also.

9   When they had heard the king, they departed; and, lo, the star, which they saw in the east, went before them, till it came and stood over where the young child was.

10   When they saw the star, they rejoiced with exceeding great joy.

11   And when they were come into the house, they saw the young child with Mary his mother, and fell down, and worshipped him: and when they had opened their treasures, they presented unto him gifts; gold, and frankincense, and myrrh.

12   And being warned of God in a dream that they should not return to Herod, they departed into their own country another way.

Nunc Dimittis

LUKE II:

29   Lord, now lettest thou thy servant depart in peace, according to thy word:

30   For mine eyes have seen thy salvation,

31   Which thou hast prepared before the face of all people;

32   A light to lighten the Gentiles, and the glory of thy people Israel.

A Christmas Prayer

O GOD, who hast illumined this most sacred night with the brightness of the true light; grant, we beseech thee, that we, who have known the mysteries of that light on earth, may enjoy also its happiness in Heaven. Through the same Lord Jesus Christ who liveth and reigneth one God world without end. *Amen.*

Acknowledgments

The publishers make grateful acknowledgment to the following: Harcourt, Brace and Company for *A Miserable, Merry Christmas*, from THE AUTOBIOGRAPHY OF LINCOLN STEFFENS, copyright, 1931, by Harcourt, Brace and Company, Inc.; Roark Bradford for *How Come Christmas?*; Charles Scribner's Sons for the two extracts from Theodore Roosevelt's LETTERS and DIARIES OF BOYHOOD AND YOUTH; Richard Evelyn Byrd for *Christmas at the North Pole*; THE ATLANTIC MONTHLY and Kenneth Irving Brown for *Christmas in Brazil*; Lady Hulse for the Christmas letter from her son, Captain Sir Edward Hamilton Hulse; Anne L. New and THE DELINEATOR for *New Christmas*; Temple Bailey for *The Candle in the Forest* from THE HOLLY HEDGE; Doubleday, Doran and Company for *The Gift of the Magi* from THE FOUR MILLION, by O. Henry, copyright, 1905, 1933, by Doubleday, Doran and Company; Heywood Broun for *The Shepherd*; Mrs. William Dean Howells for her husband's story *Christmas Every Day*; Ruth Sawyer for *The Wee Red Cap* from THIS WAY TO CHRISTMAS; Albert Bigelow Paine for *Christmas at the Hollow Tree Inn* from THE HOLLOW TREE AND BIG WOODS BOOK; Charles Scribner's Sons for *Jest 'Fore Christmas*, by Eugene Field; Percival Wilde and D. Appleton-Century Company for *Alias Santa Claus*; Coningsby Dawson for *The Seventh Christmas*; Charles Scribner's Sons for *Keeping Christmas* from THE SPIRIT OF CHRISTMAS by Henry Van Dyke.

Special thanks are due to Dr. Becket Gibbs for his arrangement of the Christmas Carols; to THE READER'S DIGEST for their condensation of *Christmas in Brazil*; and to Alice Moss for her dramatization of *The Seventh Christmas*.

INDEX OF TITLES, AUTHORS AND CHRISTMAS LORE